TRANQUILITY WITHOUT PILLS

*All About
Transcendental Meditation*

JHAN ROBBINS
and
DAVID FISHER

The Complete How-to Guide to the
Famous TM Method of Total Relaxation:
What It Is, How You Learn It,
Why It Works—and Its Effects on Tension,
Sex, Overweight, Sleep, Work Efficiency,
Drug Abuse, Smoking, Drinking,
and Much More

BANTAM BOOKS · TORONTO · NEW YORK · LONDON

TRANQUILITY WITHOUT PILLS

*A Bantam Book / published by arrangement with
Peter H. Wyden, Inc.*

PRINTING HISTORY

*Wyden edition published June 1972
2nd printing . . . . . August 1972
3rd printing . . September 1972
4th printing . . . . November 1972
Bantam edition published May 1973*

2nd printing
3rd printing

*Bantam Books are published by Bantam Books, Inc., a National
General company. Its trade-mark, consisting of the words "Bantam
Books" and the portrayal of a bantam, is registered in the United
States Patent Office and in other countries. Marca Registrada.
Bantam Books, Inc., 666 Fifth Avenue, New York, N.Y. 10019.*

PRINTED IN THE UNITED STATES OF AMERICA

THE EXPERTS REPORT ON TM . . .

"Transcendental Meditation is easily learned and produces significant physiological changes."
—Dr. Keith Wallace, Harvard University Medical School, in *The American Journal of Physiology*

"[TM] increased energy and efficiency . . . increased calmness and decreased physical and mental tensions . . . increased creativity, productivity, discrimination, intuitiveness, and concentration."
—Dr. Demetri P. Kanellakos, Stanford Research Institute

"The name [TM] turned me off at first, but in February 1971 I became a meditator . . . My blood pressure went down 10 points; my wife said my disposition improved a great deal; and the minor stresses and strains of life around Washington didn't bother me anymore."
—Maj. Gen. Franklin M. Davis, Commandant, U.S. Army War College

---

"The [TM] subjects decreased their use of hard alcoholic beverages and cigarette smoking . . . significantly decreased or stopped abusing drugs."
—Herbert Benson, M.D., Harvard University Medical School, before a U.S. House of Representatives Committee

To our parents,
who helped us transcend

An appreciation to:

Dr. Francis Driscoll, Joseph Clarke,
Major General Franklin Davis, Jerry Jarvis,
Jack Forem, Susan Hall,
Dr. Philip Barnes, Janet Hoffman,
Dr. Joseph O'Donnell, Michael Hill,
Josefa Stuart, Janice Castro,
and the hundreds of other admirable people
we met during our investigation
of transcendental meditation.

Foreword

When our publisher, Peter H. Wyden, asked us to write a book about transcendental meditation, we were skeptical about something that sounded like an instant cure-all philosophy made famous by the Beatles and Mia Farrow. However, we agreed to do some preliminary research.

We were quite surprised by what we learned and the preliminary research turned into a major investigation. We conducted interviews with scientists, meditators, and scoffers; analyzed stacks of scientific research reports; visited dozens of transcendental-meditation centers; tape-recorded the experiences of many meditators; and finally became meditators ourselves.

The deeper we delved into the subject, the more convinced we became that it had much relief to offer to our stress-ridden society. So we are pleased that this book developed into exactly what we had hoped: *a handbook of transcendental meditation.*

It is not intended for the veteran meditator. It is for the inquisitive, skeptical person who is interested in discovering just what transcendental meditation is all about. We believe that when you can have finished reading it, you will understand TM; how it can be learned in remarkably little time; how it has worked for others; and why it may do for you what it is doing for us: helping us cope with the emotional and physical strains of everyday living.

We don't think you have to be like the manager of a Maryland supermarket who told us rather too uncritically: "Transcendental meditation is like the instant cake mixes I sell. My customers are always asking me for explanations of how they work. I tell them, 'I don't understand how they work—but they do!'"

There *is* a way to understand, and here it is.

JR
DF

Contents

1

What Is
Transcendental
Meditation?

• A thirty-three-year-old executive secretary in Washington, D.C., says, "I felt completely alone in the world. All alone—drowning, groping for help, wanting to live, yet not being able to cope for even one minute—so miserable and scared of everything—always crying. Then I found transcendental meditation. The change has been fantastic. I enjoy everything and I'm not afraid of anything. At last I'm free."

• "My wife told me I was a lousy lover," said a forty-two-year-old New Jersey dentist. "One of the men I play golf with said that transcendental meditation would really help. So, in desperation, I tried it. It has! Now my problem is keeping my wife from telling everybody about the dramatic improvement in our sex lives."

• In Dayton, Ohio, a thirty-year-old housewife says, "I would definitely say my whole life changed the day I started meditating. I have become more stable in my own self, thoughts, and feelings. My health is better, I'm happier, and my coordination and perception are noticeably improved."

• A twenty-two-year-old student at a California university, who had been taking drugs for four years, discovered transcendental meditation. "I no longer have a need for drugs. I've become a respectable member of society. My confidence and self-respect have returned. My professors tell me that I'm now a good student. I owe it all to meditation."

• In Pennsylvania, a sixty-seven-year-old female alcoholic suddenly stopped her steady drinking. "I can't fit into words the thanks I have for transcendental meditation. I thought my life was over, but now I feel it's just beginning. I stopped being a fifth-a-day drinker. Now I only sip some wine occasionally."

• A Chicago car salesman told us: "The people connected with transcendental meditation are always smiling. Not phony smiles, but real happy ones that sort of show they're glad to be alive. I guess that's what started me meditating."

These statements sound far-fetched and too good to be true. Most of them resemble the famous advertisement that amused our grandparents: "I was a ninety-eight-pound weakling. Then . . ." For the more than 100,000 Americans who meditate daily, these cases are by now familiar, for they, too, are in the forefront of an extraordinarily exciting and rewarding movement.

Most others either have no knowledge of transcendental meditation or else equate the name with the Beatles. Mia Farrow. Gurus. The Maharishi. A tour with the Beach Boys. Flop, failure, fadeout!

Just what *is* transcendental meditation?

It started appearing in the news in 1967 when John, Paul, George, and Ringo heard a then somewhat obscure Indian guru speak at a London hotel and announced, "This is for us!"

Within a year most major magazines and Sunday supplements had published articles about the movement and its leader, Maharishi Mahesh Yogi. They printed sensational details about the Svengali relationship of the Maharishi to the Beatles and other stars of the entertainment world. Then, almost as quickly as transcendental meditation arrived, it seemed to fade—another fad gone the way of the coonskin cap and hula hoops.

Almost.

In 1970 fresh reports about transcendental meditation began to appear—but this time they did not originate with lay enthusiasts. This time they came from serious scientists. Throughout the country studies had been going on, and when the results were announced TM took on new significance.

In California, Dr. Demetri Kanellakos, a senior researcher at Stanford Research Institute, collected evidence showing that subjects who meditated have "increased energy and efficiency. . . . increased calmness and decreased physical and mental tensions. . . . increased creativity, productivity, discrimination, intuitiveness and concentration (by getting better grades in school for example)."

Dr. Robert Keith Wallace, a physiologist now at Harvard University Medical School, announced that, during meditation, subjects entered a unique state of consciousness that was distinguished by highly beneficial effects on the human body: significant decreases in oxygen consumption and carbon dioxide elimination, cardiac output, heart rate, and respiratory rate. Skin resistance (which decreases when stress is present) *increased* as a result of meditation, and the brain produced more pleasant alpha waves than normal.

According to Dr. Wallace, people who meditate actually become healthier. In a three hundred ninety-four-subject survey, 67 percent reported significant improvement in physical health, and 84 percent said their mental health had improved.

"The fact that transcendental meditation is easily learned and produces significant physiological changes," Dr. Wallace summed up in *The American Journal of Physiology*, "gives it certain advantages over other . . . techniques."

Meanwhile, at the University of California in Los Angeles, W. Thomas Winquist conducted a questionnaire study on the effect of transcendental meditation on drug abusers. His study involved one hundred forty-three subjects. All had been smoking marijuana when they began meditating. Eventually 84 percent stopped (for a minimum of three months). An even higher percentage of the one hundred eleven subjects who were using hallucinogens—86 percent—ceased using these drugs; and 86 percent of the forty-two addicts of hard drugs also stopped using these narcotics.

After conducting similar, though far more extensive, examinations, Dr. Herbert Benson, an assistant professor at Harvard Medical School, told the United States House of Representatives Committee on Crime about his results. They were nothing short of astounding.

"Eighteen hundred sixty-two students formed the basis of this study," he testified. "These subjects significantly decreased or stopped abusing drugs; decreased or stopped engaging in drug selling activity; and changed their attitudes in the direction of discouraging others from abusing drugs after starting transcendental meditation."

Dr. Benson also told the committee: "The subjects decreased their use of hard alcoholic beverages and cigarette smoking." (Test results will be found on page 121.)

A young soldier who had been meditating for sixteen months—and is part of the fast-growing number of meditators in the military—experienced a typical reaction. He said: "When I started, I was smoking a pack a day, but as I meditated I started smoking less and less. The desire gradually disappeared. By the time I reached the end of a cigarette it really tasted bad, I became sick if I tried one. I just couldn't take it." And as for drinking, he said: "I can really enjoy a drink or two, but I don't have the desire to get drunk any more. I don't need it to enjoy life."

In other tests, Dr. Benson showed that TM provides more deep rest during one twenty-minute session than a person gets in six hours of sleep. Twice-a-day meditation provides more deep rest than an entire night's sleep.

Although no studies have yet been conducted concerning weight loss, many men and women have started losing weight as soon as they began meditating. A Long Island, N.Y., housewife lost fifteen pounds after she started on TM. "I was a compulsive eater," she remembers. "Even though I didn't want them, I would devour any leftovers. Candy, too. I just couldn't bear to see an open box of candy without stuffing my mouth. I had this neurotic desire to eat, eat, eat. As soon as I began meditating, it disappeared."

The person who isn't hungry but constantly goes to the refrigerator looking for snacks, the man who chain smokes or drinks to excess, and the student who uses drugs, often picks up such habits in an attempt to relieve stress and tension. For many people, transcendental meditation has replaced these crutches—enabling them to keep the refrigerator closed, the bottle unopened, the marijuana not used.

More and more scientists are taking a long and serious look at the possibilities TM holds. And more and more prominent people began lending their names to the movement. Buckminster Fuller, the innovator, planner, and creator of the geodesic dome, paid extravagant tribute to the Maharishi.

"You could not meet with Maharishi for a minute," he said, "without recognizing his integrity. You look in his eyes and there it is . . . he manifests love."

An army general announced he had become a meditator and was actively attempting to convince the military that meditation would benefit drug-addicted soldiers. Colleges and universities—Yale, Stanford, UCLA, Colorado, and dozens of others—offered courses in the study of transcendental meditation.

If TM had begun to be touted like a new miracle drug, the Maharishi quickly put extravagant claims to rest. He explained, *"Transcendental meditation is a natural technique which allows the conscious mind to experience increasingly more subtle states of thought until the source of thought, the unlimited reservoir of energy and creative intelligence, is reached. This simple practice expands the capacity of the conscious mind and a man is able to use his full potential in all fields of thought and action."*

Although the name "transcendental meditation" may accurately explain the process, it sounds so cultish that it tends to scare away some potential meditators. The Maharishi seems to be aware of this, and once said, "Perhaps many people have been turned away by the name but it's a perfect description of what it is."

According to official doctrine as disseminated by the Students International Meditation Society (SIMS), the main TM teaching group in this country, transcendental meditation develops creative intelligence and improves clarity of perception at all levels of experience. It is practiced a few minutes each morning and evening. These sessions permit the body to gain deep rest while the mind expands in awareness. TM is unique, natural, and facilitates full development of the individual. It can be easily learned and enjoyed by just about everyone.

"The technique is as ancient as mankind," says the SIMS literature, "and is universal in its application. At this time in our history it is being brought to the world by Maharishi Mahesh Yogi."

In theory, the mind itself travels to more refined levels of mental activity, reaching the so-called "source of thought." The experience obtained while making this trip enables the individual to expand his awareness and understand more about the workings of his own intelligence, thus making more of his mental potential available for his use.

The effects of this "trip" can be physically documented, as the Harvard research has shown. This evidence documents that the body is in a state of profoundly deep rest. Yet, according to brain-wave tests performed by electroencephalograph (EEG), the mind is fully awake and totally able to respond to stimuli. The resulting feeling is described by meditators as extremely relaxing and refreshing, physically as well as mentally.

"We feel healthier and happier," they explain.

In most other forms of meditation, withdrawal from everyday activities is usually considered necessary. By dramatic contrast, the main purpose of TM is to enhance those everyday activities as you go along your usual routine. TM as taught by followers of the Maharishi Mahesh Yogi therefore requires absolutely no change of life style.

"We have been told," the Maharishi said, "that we must not be material. But it is natural to be material. It is impossible not to be material. Our bodies and our senses are material. Indeed, a material basis for spiritual development is essential. We want to bring forth an inner serenity, and not a horror of the material."

Leaders of the TM movement are quick to point out that their technique is not in any way similar to a religion. Nor is it intended to replace any religious beliefs. If anything, it acts to strengthen an individual's belief. A meditator said, "By the time you reach cosmic consciousness, the final goal of meditators, you've had to do a tremendous amount of introspection. You've really seen how the whole human factory works and you're forced to ask yourself: Why? Almost inevitably, meditators look to the Supreme Being."

No one is required to declare a belief in TM, in the

Maharishi, or even in the possible effects of the technique in order for it to work. *It works in spite of an individual's disbelief or skepticism.* And there is much skepticism.

The somewhat vague promise of better health and greater happiness has been offered by a bewilderingly large (and often preposterous) variety of people and products for hundreds of years. And, with extremely few exceptions, it has remained unfilled. Why should it be believed in this case? The growth of the movement inspires confidence. So does the medical evidence. No question about it: TM is the most successful of all the Eastern philosophies to be imported to the West.

TM's word-of-mouth advertising is impressive. Most people first come to a TM center on the advice of friends. Although there is a flow of literature from the centers, knowledge of the movement has spread mostly by way of satisfied users. People have seen TM work for their friends and therefore expect it to work for them.

Uncritical enthusiasm aside, TM has been indisputably successful. During our research we heard meditator after meditator cite evidence of personal self-improvement and credit TM for the change. In fact, the hardest problem we encountered in preparing this book was trying to obtain a balance of opinion. Even some of the scoffers had kind words for TM. A professor of biophysics at Columbia University said, "If *Scientific American* prints a favorable article about transcendental meditation, I suppose I have to rethink my objections."

We expected practicing meditators to defend TM but not as vociferously as they actually did. It reached the point where we had to do detective work to dig up negative stories and reports.

This is not to say that transcendental meditation is effective in every case. It is absolutely not a cure-all. Some people complained of buzzing in the ears, dizziness, and other discomforts after meditating. Others said they gained nothing from the process. But these were the limited few, and we had to search hard to find them.

Transcendental meditation is not a new process. Its history is less than precise, but it can best be traced through the Maharishi Mahesh Yogi.

The Maharishi was born in 1918, the third of four children of a forest ranger in the employ of the Central Provinces Government of what was then British India. His name was Mahesh Prasad Varma and his family belonged to the Kayastha caste.

Details of his life tend to be a bit sketchy because Hindus who renounce the material world to devote their lives to asceticism, religion, and their soul's salvation consider themselves newly born. They take a new name and will not divulge any details about their early life. Although the Maharishi has conformed to this tradition, he defends materialism for others.

His followers have compiled something of an official biography, which reports his graduation from Allahabad University with a degree in physics in 1942. According to this biography, he took a job in a factory and set out to learn Sanskrit. He was expected to follow the accepted life style of members of his caste and become a merchant, shopkeeper, scribe or clerk. His parents were in the process of arranging a suitable marriage for him when, in the early 1940s, he met Swami Brahmananda Saraswati, the Jagadguru Bhagwan Shankaracharya or Guru Dev (divine teacher), one of the four major religious leaders of India. It is at this point that all sources begin to agree.

Mahesh was immediately taken with the Jagadguru and asked to be accepted as a disciple. Guru Dev agreed, but only if Mahesh had the consent of his parents. At first his father refused to agree. Finally he relented. Legend has it that the Guru Dev had a long talk with Mahesh's parents and finally explained, "This son of yours is not going to live in your house. It will be better if you give him your consent." They did. Mahesh left his home and never returned to live there again.

Mahesh stayed with the Shankarachayra for thirteen and a half years and quickly developed into the monk's favorite disciple. When the time came for his master to "leave his body," (Hindus believe that great spiritual leaders die only in a physical sense; their spiritual essence lives on).

The old man supposedly said to his pupil, "My time has come to leave this body. There is only one thing I have not done. Because of the cares and responsibilities of my position as Jagadguru and Shankaracharya of Joytir Math, much of my time has been lost which I should have devoted to achieving the giving of peace to ordinary people. I leave this task to you, and to fulfill it you must evolve some simple form of meditation which anyone can learn and practice."

The Maharishi-to-be agreed and went into a two-year period of seclusion in the Himalaya Mountains, emerging with a process that he called transcendental meditation. TM is adapted from a technique that was used several hundred years before the birth of Christ. The Maharishi took those parts he thought most important and streamlined them for the jet age. What developed is an easy-to-learn method that he began teaching in southern India.

But then he realized that he was making frus-

tratingly slow progress. "One fine morning," he remembers, "I thoughtfully reviewed the work done
and calculated how much time it would take for the
whole world to learn the method. At this rate it would
take forever!" He decided to expand.

In 1956 he made his first tour through India,
asking the question, "When a man has a right to supreme joy, why should he not take it?" And taking it,
he said, was as easy as learning transcendental meditation. In 1958 some Indian businessmen working in
Rangoon, Burma, brought him there to speak. Thus
began the first of his eight world tours.

Being quite pragmatic, the Maharishi decided
to bring his message to those people "who are in the
habit of accepting things quickly," so in 1959 he
came to the West. After establishing the International Meditation Society in London, he settled down
to begin teaching TM. He also took full advantage
of the western world's vast communication systems,
using television, radio, photography, and public relations to help him spread word of his method. Slowly
but steadily, the name he gave to the organization
began to grow. And grow. And grow.

By 1971 transcendental meditation was firmly
entrenched in fifty-one nations and in every section
of the United States. He himself had become something of a celebrity and had appeared on almost
every major American television and radio talk show.
The overwhelming success of the movement suggested
that he leave his ashram (a place where meditation
is taught) in Rishikesh, India, and settle, at least
temporarily, on the beautiful island of Mallorca, in
Spain, where his headquarters is still located.

The Maharishi has suffered setbacks along the
way. He has been falsely accused by other Indian

gurus of living in a style totally out of line with true Hindu tradition, of being publicity conscious and of serving up his own brand of "instant yoga" to entertainment personalities. Although his life style may indeed be luxurious by traditional Hindu tradition, he lives quite simply by Western standards. When traveling, he occupies a single room in a middle-class hotel and usually takes his meals in his room.

The Beatles, who helped him gain worldwide attention, did in fact desert him, accusing him of being too materially oriented, although three of them continue to meditate. Again, his followers defended his actions by saying the Maharishi is only doing whatever is necessary to help the movement grow. Perhaps the low point came in mid-1968, when the Maharishi scheduled a three-week tour of the United States with a singing group known as the Beach Boys. The tour was canceled just after it started, because of poor attendance, and the Maharishi went back to India.

The major accusation leveled at the Maharishi is based on the fact that, although SIMS and other groups are legal, nonprofit, educational organizations, the movement does generate a large income from student fees. Many people believe that the Maharishi is making a considerable profit from his movement, but the facts do not seem to bear that out. The entire income of the movement is promptly reinvested in upkeep of the TM centers, salaries, and incidental expenses, such as travel for teachers. "I have no pockets," he says.

Physically, the Maharishi is not at all impressive. He is a very small man and has a long, scraggly white beard. His hair is usually uncombed and flows down onto his shoulders. He normally dresses in a white silk dhoti which Major General Franklin M. Davis, commandant of the U.S. Army War College and a meditator himself, has described jokingly, as looking quite like a white bedsheet. His voice is high and lilting and sounds incredibly like a thirty-three and one-third rpm. record being played at seventy-eight.

But two things stand out about the Maharishi— or the Hindu monk from the Shankaracharya tradition, lifelong celibate, spiritual and active leader of the International Meditation Society, Students International Meditation Society, and the Spiritual Regeneration Movement, as he is officially known; his affable nature and his eyes. The eyes that Buckminster Fuller spoke about are piercing, and he possesses a great American trait—the ability to look someone squarely in the eyes while speaking to them. Those who have met him come away somewhat dazzled and talk about "the honesty" in his eyes.

He is extremely friendly and has a good sense of humor. When someone asked him if it were not true that he was a rich man he replied, "Yes, ha, ha, it is true, ha ha, I am a rich man. I have cars, and airplanes, and I even have my own personal submarine, painted yellow." This reference to the Beatles' hit, *The Yellow Submarine*, is not the stuff that nightclub comedians are made out of, but acceptable considering the source.

The Maharishi has been described by many meditators as "everyone's best friend," and he seems to come across as that. In talking with an individual he has the ability to make that person feel that he is the most important human being in the world.

The Maharishi is a celibate, a vegetarian, and takes absolutely no drugs. "Unless," as he gigglingly told Johnny Carson one late night, "the doctors prescribe them." He does not, however, require any meditator to emulate his own ways. "Transcendental meditation does not reject the material world," he told an audience in New York; "it merely helps to acquire greater happiness within it."

This method that he named transcendental meditation, and upon which he has based his entire program for greater happiness in the everyday world, works on many different levels. As a physical process it is relaxing, even when performed only sporadically. As a mental process it yields cumulative effects that do seem to add up to a better life for the meditator. As a physiological process it has shown an ability to improve an individual's health. And as an overall system, it seems to fulfill a certain need in an individual that heretofore had been fulfilled by something else, in many, many cases that "something else" being drugs or alcohol.

Physically, TM is an enjoyable experience. Virginia Cook, a researcher at the University of Pittsburgh, provided an enticing description of meditation: "You are swimming in the stormy Atlantic. The rough, choppy sea batters you until you feel like Joe Frazier's sparring partner. You are bruised and exhausted, but suddenly you dive to the very bottom of the ocean floor.

"All is quiet there. All is serene. You see fish and plants more beautiful than women at an opening night. Finally, you swim into the intoxicating blackness of the ocean deep.

"When you surface the storm is over, the sun is shining. You are deeply rested from the quiet of the ocean, and you are excited because you have touched unknown depths. You swim easily now, the concrete water beneath supporting you."

TM is based on the natural tendency of the mind

to move toward greater happiness and pleasure. During meditation, for example, someone in the next room might begin playing a favorite song of yours. One's awareness is automatically drawn toward this pleasing experience. In other types of meditation you would force your mind to concentrate on keeping that music *out* of your mind, lest your meditation be disturbed. During transcendental meditation your mind is expected to follow whatever is most natural and most pleasant; in this case simply listen to, and enjoy the music.

After each period of meditation, even if you have not been meditating on a regular basis, you should normally feel relaxed and energetic.

As a cumulative mental activity, then, TM acts to remove tension, frustration, and worry. The entire process is based on the fact that man stores his feelings of stress inside himself, and this stress forces him to act in certain, often antisocial ways. Through meditation, these pockets of stress are released, which enables meditators to enjoy a much freer, much more fulfilled life than they previously did. In other words, the longer you follow a regular schedule of meditation twice a day in the manner that we will describe, the more able you will be to act, free from the weight of accumulated stress.

With this principle in mind, Maharishi even insists that transcendental meditation can lead to world peace. "From my analysis," he says, "it is not the military that creates the wars; it's the civilians who remain frustrated, tense, and worried, who are creating an atmosphere of tension." It follows, he feels, that if the "atmosphere of tension" were removed, so would the cause of wars.

Maharishi's claim that TM is the method that

can eliminate frustration, worry, and tension is backed by innumerable examples of people who have done just that. A dealer at Las Vegas gambling tables joined a transcendental meditation group when he felt he was nearing his own breaking point: "The public was getting on my nerves so much that I was just about ready to quit my job. Then I began meditating and now my job is easier. I'm simply much more tolerant than I was before."

A twenty-one-year-old musician in Chicago discovered the same thing about himself: "Before I started meditating I was nervous, high-strung, tense, and had many problems with drug use. When I started TM these problems immediately became smaller, and with a year of meditation, have completely disappeared."

Even General Davis, as he told us in an extended interview, found TM tremendously helpful in eliminating stress. "My grandmother used to say I had a very even disposition," he said laughing. "I was always mean. I don't think I was quite that bad, but it certainly isn't true anymore. I don't let the everyday minor problems bother me and I am more tolerant of the people I work with."

World peace? A wistful hope.

Inner peace? Attainable.

There is no question about the impressive physiological impact of transcendental meditation. As Maharishi points out, for every mental action there is a physical reaction. As we have shown, science has successfully measured the physical reaction to meditation as well as the physical after-effects of TM.

In their studies, for example, Drs. Benson and Wallace found that oxygen consumption decreased, cardiac output decreased, skin resistance,* (an indicator of stress) increased, and the lactate ion concentration in the blood (believed to be a partial cause of stress feelings) decreased. Dr. Wallace made a point of noting that these changes are unlike any of those occurring during wakefulness, sleeping, and dreaming, the three major states of human existence generally recognized by physiologists. This fourth state of existence, called a transcendental state, has long been discussed in the mystic literature of many cultures. To the yogi it is known as "samadhi"; the Zen Buddhist calls it "satori"; and early Christian mystic Meister Eckhart called it "the cloud of unknowing."

At the University of Texas in Austin, two researchers conducted studies that indicated that the reaction time of meditators was significantly faster than the response of nonmeditators. When they tested response to a light signal, they found that meditators reacted about 30 percent faster on the average than nonmeditators.

At the El Paso campus of the University of Texas, it was discovered that meditators are less irritable and jittery than nonmeditators. Dr. David Orme-Johnson, using measurements of skin resistance, showed that meditators stopped reacting to repeated loud noises (about the level of a boiler factory) much sooner than did nonmeditators. It took the nonmeditators

---

* During skin-resistance tests, delicate sensors are attached to the body and a slight electric current is sent from one sensor to another. This current comes from a constant voltage source. The ratio of the voltage supplied to the current obtained is proportional to the resistance of the skin. Tension, anxiety, and nervousness cause an individual to sweat and thus contribute to a lower skin resistance. Generally, the more relaxed and calm a person is, the higher his resistance will be.

about thirty to thirty-five repetitions to get used to the noise and stop producing changes on the GSR scale. Meditators, on the other hand, accepted the noise without reaction after a maximum of fifteen trials. The doctor also discovered that the longer a person had been meditating, the fewer trials it took for him to get used to the noise, evidence of the cumulative value of TM.

Behavior is also favorably affected by TM. Psychological tests given at the University of Cincinnati would seem to show that meditators, as a group, are happier than nonmeditators. A "self-actualization" test was designed to show to what degree an individual was using his full potential. Thirty-five students participated in the study. Fifteen were then initiated into TM and, two months later, all were retested. The meditators scored significantly higher in six of twelve indexes of self-actualization. The other students remained about the same.

In short, an abundance of evidence indicates that certain changes do occur in the body because of transcendental meditation. In every test thus far, these changes have been generally positive. Although there is still a need for much more experimentation, there can be little doubt about the therapeutic effects of TM.

The relationship between transcendental meditation and drugs (as well as alcohol and cigarette smoking) is an interesting one, and thoroughly examined in the Question & Answer section of this book.

Because drugs act on the nervous system, initiates are asked not to take any drug for 15 days before their initiation—unless prescribed by a physician. This does not hold true for alcohol or cigarettes. After a person is initiated into TM, it is left up to him to de-

cide whether he would like to return to drugs or
continue drinking or smoking. No claims are made
that TM will replace the need for these psychological
crutches, but, in a vast number of cases, this seems
to be exactly the case.

TM has been found to be an extremely effective
means of eliminating drug abuse. Studies by Dr.
Benson and Dr. Wallace showed that a remarkably
high percentage of subjects totally stopped using all
drugs twenty-one months after they had started meditation. For example, of a test group 80 percent used
marijuana before beginning meditation. Within
twenty-one months that number was down to 12
percent. (See Q&A for more detailed statistics). Of
the same group, 60 percent used hard liquor; within
twenty-one months the number was 25 percent. Before meditation, 48 percent smoked cigarettes, a number that was reduced to 16 percent after twenty-one
months. It was tests like these that first interested
General Davis, then head of an army program designed to come up with an answer to the military's
drug-abuse problem, in TM. It convinced him that
TM may be an answer for the army's problems with
heavy users of drugs.

Although members of the Students International
Meditation Society (and the other TM organizations)
do not emphasize the success TM has had as a drug-
abuse cure—they are afraid that such publicity would
scare away nondrug users—the evidence is impressive
that TM is effective as a drug-alcohol-cigarette substitute.

The proponents of TM maintain that meditation
dissolves an individual's inner deposits of stress and
brings strength and energy to the surface, where these
assets can be utilized. An individual can then deter-

mine his own "true potential" or "creative intelligence"; increase his own awareness of the obstacles around him, and gain in his ability to deal with them.

It all happens in the astonishingly simple process known as transcendental meditation, or, as one reporter dubbed it, "a course in how to succeed spiritually without really trying."

2

How to Meditate

The Maharishi has said it again and again: Learning to meditate is as easy as learning to brush your teeth. He points out that nothing complicated is involved. It is simply a matter of following instructions from a properly trained teacher.

After you have read this book you should know all you need to know to meditate. We do not, however, suggest that you use what you learn to attempt to experiment on your own with transcendental meditation. We firmly believe, as we were taught by our initiators (and as they were taught by the Maharishi), that the system should be imparted by someone trained as a TM teacher. As you will see in our detailed accounts of the experiences of meditators, there are personal questions about you own experience that are best answered for you personally so you can fully enjoy TM. And these should be answered by a qualified individual. Since TM is a process that affects the physiology of the body and involves total use of the nervous system, it should not be used without proper instruction.

"Transcendental meditation cannot be ground out by mass production," the Maharishi has explained. "It cannot be turned into a system that anyone can learn by following some sort of 'recipe'—it isn't shrimp curry, or steak and kidney pie, or a sukiyaki dish."

Cynics have suggested that since TM is so easy to learn, the only reason why everyone is advised to study at a TM center is to enable the organization to collect a fee. This is simply not true. As we will show, individual follow-up is necessary during the initiation stage. Besides, the fees are so low that they only enable the movement to keep growing.

Learning how to meditate is not complicated. Twice daily, preferably in the morning and evening before eating, all you have to do is sit quietly and let your mind go wherever it wants. Normally, individuals are advised to meditate for two twenty-minute periods each day. There is no risk in meditating longer, but since TM is a preparation for activity, not an activity in itself, longer meditation might lead to withdrawal from the world, not participation in it. This is where TM differs dramatically from most other forms of meditation. The others tend to encourage withdrawal. (The problem of meditating too long often comes up with young children. They may enjoy meditation so much that they attempt to practice it for hours at a time. This must be quickly discouraged.)

Inevitably, according to the Maharishi, when you let your mind wander freely, it will drift in the direction of things that please you greatly. If eating a rare filet mignon is what makes you happiest, a picture of a juicy steak may pop into your head. Or you may find yourself thinking about the last time you made love. Or you may remember a long-forgotten snowball fight of many years ago. The important thing is not to direct your mind in any specific direction.

"Just let the mind flow freely," says the Maharishi.

It is easiest to meditate while sitting in a quiet, comfortable place, but you really can meditate anywhere. While most beginning meditators prefer relative quiet, veterans often meditate on a bus or train.

"The nature of the mind is to move onto a field of greater happiness," the Maharishi says, "and in the innermost region of one's being, bliss is present. This bliss draws the mind to it, naturally."

The "path" to this bliss is straight and wide. The most important thing during transcendental meditation is to avoid concentrating on anything in particular. Concentration holds the mind at one level, and will not allow it to submerge into a deeper level of consciousness.

During an individual's initiation ceremony he is assigned something that sounds like a nonsense syllable, called a mantra. Critics say that Alice in Wonderland would have been an ideal meditator since the mantra often sounds like jabberwocky, yet the mantra is of major help in placing your mind in a very relaxed state. It is actually a Sanskrit sound and may or may not have meaning. Most Eastern philosophies propound that each person's consciousness pulsates in a certain rhythm, and this word, or sound, is specifically selected by a specially trained teacher for its ability to pulsate with that particular, quite individual rhythm.

The Maharishi emphasized the importance of the mantra by explaining that, "Each man meditates on a given word, suitable to the impulses of the man. The sound of the word is important, not the meaning, but the quality of the sound." Since there are only a limited number of acceptable mantras, far more than one person has the same mantra.*

An individual should never repeat his mantra out loud, meditators are advised; to enunciate it would place it on a "grosser" state than is desirable.

"Om" is an example of a mantra that has been considered a universal sound. But TM teachers emphasize that there can be no one mantra for everyone, and the potential side effects of an improper mantra can be negative.

It is very important during meditation that an individual does not try to define the meaning of the word itself, but rather repeats the sound. After sitting down in a comfortable place, a would-be meditator should first close his eyes and start repeating the mantra silently.

"Transcendental meditation is a practice first and a theory afterwards," a veteran meditator explained. "It is essential at the beginning that an individual does not think intellectually at all."

Slowly, as the meditation becomes deeper and

---

* Although we have strong doubts about the theory of "one man, one mantra," there is little physical evidence to substantiate either side of the question. In our cases, the assigned mantras have worked well, but we believe that we might have obtained the same results by using any of the many mantras that are in use. Joseph Clarke, the SIMS regional coordinator, explained what makes a mantra effective: "I was lecturing in Rhode Island and a young man explained how he tried to use his wife's instruction for his own meditation, probably trying to save the fee. Unfortunately, because he didn't have the right guidance, the results were unsatisfactory and there were side effects: irritability, withdrawal and lack of energy. Eventually, he decided to get his personal instruction and found a positive, dramatic change in his experience."

deeper, an individual may actually experience waves of relaxation sweeping across his body. Some people compare the sensation to a gentle massage. Things he hadn't thought about in years may suddenly pop into his mind and just as quickly disappear. All this occurs very naturally, effortlessly. The feeling during deep meditation is actually a "nonfeeling," a total sense of relaxation, without awareness that the process of meditation is going on.

Whenever the mind returns to the conscious level —the meditator knows this because at that point he realizes he is in the midst of meditation—the key is to return to the mantra. This may occur repeatedly during one session. Theoretically, each time an individual finds himself returning to consciousness he has released a pocket of stress.

George Harrison, formerly of the Beatles, offered one of the best explanations of the process while talking to David Frost on American television. "You know," he said, "you just sort of sit there and let your mind go wherever it's going. Doesn't matter what you're thinking about. Just let it go, and then you introduce the mantra to take over from the thought. You don't will it or use your will power. If you find yourself thinking, then the moment you realize you've been thinking about things again, you replace that thought with the mantra again.

"Sometimes you can go on and find that you haven't even had the mantra in your mind. It's just been a complete blank. But then you reach that point [*total relaxation and mindlessness*] because it's beyond all experience. Then it's down there and that level is timeless, spaceless, so you could be there for five minutes and come out; you don't actually know how long you've been there, because it's just the actual level of contact of that [*inner peace and under-standing*] and then coming back out to the gross level, like this level [*consciousness*], and you bring that with you" [*stress and tension are gone*].

That deep point he was talking about is what the Maharishi calls the Transcendental State of Being. "This state lies beyond all seeing, hearing, touching, smelling, and tasting—beyond all thinking and beyond all feeling. This state of the unmanifested, absolute, pure consciousness of Being is the ultimate state of life.

"Only when sensory perception has come to an end," the Maharishi continued, "can this transcendental field of Being be reached."

An individual does not reach this state each time he meditates. Sometimes he may sit there for the full, recommended twenty-minute period, thinking he is fully awake and aware. The time may go slowly and an individual may find his thoughts during meditation centering on something as exotic as what to have for dinner. During other meditations, however, all sense of time and place may be lost completely.

The twenty minutes may flash by as if they are a minisecond. Surprisingly, most meditators learn to judge the end of the twenty-minute period quickly. However, it is quite acceptable to sneak an occasional look at the clock.

When the time period has ended, the meditator should sit quietly for at least two or three minutes, very slowly opening his eyes. Because TM physiologically puts an individual into a fourth state of consciousness, a sudden, totally unexpected sound may have a jarring effect; anticipated sounds usually do not bother you at all. For example, after the metabolic rate has slowed down considerably and the nervous system has relaxed, the surprise ring of the telephone strikes a loud and discordant note. It may cause a classic case of a nervous, churning stomach. For this same reason, an individual should not end his meditation abruptly.

Many questions may be asked at this point. Why, for example, if the mind is brought to the level of its greatest happiness, would it return to a lesser level? The answer is simple: previous training that runs counter to the TM philosophy. Because it is not used to functioning in the physiological state of deep meditation—which involves a natural decrease of oxygen intake, among other changes—the body can only sustain the changes for a certain length of time. Of course, the longer an individual meditates, the longer the mind can stay on this level of deep consciousness, until a level of skill is reached at which the mind can stay on this plane of total relaxation constantly, even during consciousness. When an individual has developed the ability to bring this deep state to the conscious level on a permanent basis, he is said to have reached cosmic consciousness, the goal of all meditators.

Now that you have learned how to meditate—don't! Get to a TM center (see page 139) if you decide that TM may be for you.

3

How Does Transcendental Meditation Work?

Although TM is supposed to relieve the body gradually of accumulated stresses and strains and bring peace and harmony to the surface, its teachers summarize this considerable task in an astonishingly simple analogy: The human body is much like a tree; as problems arise at the surface, they are made visible by movements or actual physical changes. But the wise gardener knows that the problems, as they appear, are only symptoms of a much greater need in the tree, the need for nourishment. And so he will take specific care of this need. And when he does that, he is treating the entire problem so that every aspect of the tree begins to become stronger and healthier.

The point of regular meditation sessions, then, is to provide constant "nourishment" to the system. This is done by striving to reach the goal of every meditator, cosmic consciousness, which is simply being able to remain at the State of Being, on a conscious level, on a permanent basis.

The process is predicated on the fact that the human body does, in fact, store stress. Dr. Demetri P. Kanellakos, the senior research engineer in radio physics at Stanford Research Institute, has been conducting investigative research on TM.

Dr. Kanellakos uses an illustration borrowed from Professor Kurt Vanselow, a scientist at Kiel University, in Germany. "Suppose I am crossing a street and suddenly a car comes hurtling at me out of nowhere," says Dr. Kanellakos, "screeching on its brakes and halting a few inches before it hits me. My heart begins to beat fast. I sweat. Adrenalin and cholesterol rush through my whole system preparing me to flee from danger. But there is no reason to run. The car didn't hit me after all.

"However, my nervous system was overwhelmed with sensory input and a lot of strain was stored biochemically in the nerves—in the same way information is stored in a computer. That part of my nervous system in which this stress is stored is no longer available to me to use. Furthermore, let's say that two weeks later I am sitting in my living room reading the paper and a car outside slams on its brakes. The stored memory of the earlier experience, triggered by the outside noise, causes my heart to beat faster and my adrenalin and cholesterol to rush through my system, just as it did before.

"The more dramatic the experience and the more profound, the more deeply it is stored in the nervous system—on more unconscious, sensitive and subtle levels, where the rest gained from sleep and dreaming cannot get at it. But during TM, the physiology of the whole body settles down to a lower and lower level, giving the body a more deep, profound rest, while the mind remains alert. Eventually I reach this level where this particular stress is stored. Since I no longer have the energy stored at that level to hold the stress, it is released, usually without my even being aware of it.

"The body," Dr. Kanellakos explains, "given the appropriate restful condition, will automatically throw off stress. The stress release will produce some physical motion in the stressed area, which in turn will produce impulses that will reach and be processed by the brain (a process called 'thinking'). Thus, the stress will be briefly experienced as a meaningless thought and will be gone. The next time you are sitting in your living room reading a paper, and you hear a car slam its brakes on, you will look up from your paper and think *a car slammed on its brakes like that when one almost hit me,* and return to the paper. Not only have you not wasted any time or energy being upset, but also you have not stored new stress for the future."

The unique ability of TM to reach these layers, and act as a release mechanism, is somewhat involved, but not really all that complicated. To have a single thought involves many different levels of consciousness. As the meditation teachers explain it, a thought begins on the most subtle level of the mind and gradually rises upward until it reaches the level of consciousness. Thoughts do not just "pop" into the mind, in other words; they begin to emerge from quite deep within the mind and, when triggered by the proper process, begin to be shaped into what we call thoughts.

The basic ingredients of the thought may lie dormant in the inner consciousness for a long time, just waiting to be shaped.

As the Maharishi says, "A thought starts from

the deepest level of consciousness, from the deepest
level of the ocean of the mind, as a bubble starts at
the bottom of the sea. As the bubble rises, it gradually becomes bigger. When it comes to the surface
of the water it is perceived as a bubble."

Many teachers of TM like to say that the mind
acts as the ocean and thoughts are the bubbles. Anything on the surface of the water (the mind) is visible; anything below remains unseen until it reaches
the surface. "Any thought at surface level," the Maharishi says "is seen consciously, and it is at this level
that thoughts are appreciated as thoughts."

Every thought, in other words, must make the
entire trip, through all levels of consciousness, even
though it is not recognized as a thought in any moments of earlier development. So, thoughts that seem
to appear "suddenly" in an individual's mind are
really not at all sudden. In all probability, they have
been developing deep in his consciousness for quite
some time.

The illustration most easily recognized by anyone
who has ever been to a transcendental-meditation
lecture is a single way line, representing the surface
of the ocean and the state of consciousness, and deep
cycles that form mountains and valleys. The peaks
of the mountains rise above sea level while the valleys
are deep in the oceans. Rising from one valley, at a
point called A, is a small bubble. As the bubble rises
to the surface—B—it gets larger and larger, until it
is many, many times larger on the surface than it was
at the depths. This diagram, obviously, represents the
thought process.

If it were possible to be aware of the thought
processes going on between point A and point B, the
power of the mind would increase tremendously.

And, according to meditators, this mind expansion is exactly what happens if an individual continues to meditate on a regular basis.

"The full mental potential is thus unfolded and the conscious capacity of the mind is increased to the maximum extent," the Maharishi says.

After continued meditation, the conscious mind will reach point A, the source of all thought, the seat of what meditators call "creative intelligence." And once that point is within the grasp of the conscious mind, the individual can consciously will his own response and act accordingly. From this point there is only one more step to go, the very biggest step of all. When the conscious mind reaches this point it has the ability to transcend it, or go beyond it, to the Absolute State of Being, a state of pure consciousness or self-awareness.

The State of Being is the very deepest state of meditation. It is that place in your mind where energy, intelligence, stability, and happiness actually have their beginnings. Since there is no stress or tension at this level, these qualities can be called pure.

Physically, Being is an inactive state that can only be reached during meditation. It exhibits characteristics much like sleep, in that an individual can only recognize he has arrived there after he has left. But many of the tests that we have discussed show that it is physiologically quite different from sleep.

Some new meditators experience Being immediately—if only for brief moments. Critics say that since Being can only be reached during meditation, what good is it?

Meditators offer a ready reply: *cosmic consciousness.*

Cosmic consciousness is defined as an active,

waking state in which all the qualities exhibited at Being are present and all stress has disappeared.

In short, the individual becomes a happy person.

Once an individual has mastered the technique of traveling down through the layers of consciousness to this source of thought, it is natural for him to reach the level where stress is stored. The creative energy generated by the process frees this stress, which in turn rises to the surface and is dissipated.

It is difficult, although certainly not impossible, for an individual to reach this Transcendental State of Being by using only what he has learned after attending the two introductory lectures and four initiation sessions. So, once an individual begins meditation there are other programs to help him progress toward this goal.

The first is called "checking," or verification of experiences. Usually, an individual should return to the place where he was initiated two weeks after finishing the four sessions. The checking process is simple and takes only a brief time. The meditator sits down with a teacher and they both discuss his experiences and any problems he has encountered. Then they meditate together. Although the practice of meditation is quite simple, according to the Maharishi, "A man needs regular confirmation of his experience in order to perfect the technique and become entirely familiar with it.

"While checking need not be frequent, once the meditation is firmly established, it is important to maintain contact with a checker whose training and experience will be available as a guide."

Checking is believed to be extremely important the further an individual progresses because, at each step, he is dealing with an ever more abstract thought process, one which will be totally unfamiliar. In addition to checking sessions, most SIMS centers hold weekly "advanced" lectures for all meditators.

Although advanced lectures are available, many meditators find they progress quite nicely without ever attending one. Others are so happy with their results that they actively seek out other meditators. Advanced lectures are attended by meditators of every age. As an individual progresses deeper into his own inner consciousness, there will be many experiences he may not understand.

These lectures are the place to ask questions and get answers. A typical session is attended by as many as fifty people. Once it begins, it is thrown open for discussion. This is the time for give and take, and often a great deal of skepticism about one point or another of the program will be expressed. After discussion there will probably be a group meditation. (It is quite easy to meditate with a large group, as long as everyone is meditating.)

In the middle of one advanced lecture the lights suddenly went out. A deep male voice from the back of the room asked whether the sudden blackout was part of a plot to help meditators meditate more deeply.

The answer was a prompt no. "You don't need lights or music or incense or a warm blanket to help you meditate," replied the teacher. "All you need is a comfortable chair, twenty minutes, and a pair of closed eyes. More than likely, the light failure is a plot by the electric company to get us to pay our bills!"

Meditation weekends are also offered. "Many religious groups call weekends 'retreats,'" explains Janet Hoffman, a pretty young New York TM instructor, "because they actually retreat into themselves. We call our weekends *'advances,'* because we are moving forward toward the state of cosmic consciousness." These two-, three- or four-day weekends consist mainly of lectures and meditation.

Advances are one of the few periods when an individual may meditate for great lengths of time, because the purpose of attending the advance is to gain a deeper understanding of meditation—and practice on the premises is necessary. The social life at an advance is secondary and the main topic of conversation is TM, and an individual's progress toward cosmic consciousness or "C.C."

Occasionally, the Maharishi conducts TM courses and naturally becomes the star attraction. Weekending meditators constantly besiege him for autographs and he tries to oblige. One slender, blonde young lady ran up to him with an outstretched lipstick, and breathlessly explained that it was all she had handy.

Gently, taking the lipstick the Maharishi smiled, bowed, and wrote, "Enjoy."

Perhaps that is the best way of describing the philosophy of transcendental meditation.

4

The Making of a Meditator

The bright, silver, square plaque proclaims this to be the residence of the "Students International Meditation Society." It is the only thing that makes the brick building at 23 Cornelia Street, New York City, distinguishable from its Greenwich Village neighbors. Cornelia Street, in keeping with the gentle vibrations of transcendental meditation, is a quiet, attractive street directly off a main thoroughfare. On the recessed door of the building is a small poster with a picture of the Maharishi and the pronouncement, "Transcendental Meditation as taught by the Maharishi Mahesh Yogi. Transcendental Meditation is a natural spontaneous technique which allows each individual to expand his conscious mind and improve all aspects of life."

That metal door opens onto a carpeted hallway and a second door with a sign that says, "Please close the door gently." Quite polite, quite in place, as is everything in this SIMS center.

It is typical of SIMS centers across the country—clean, quiet and filled with smiling faces (an unofficial house rule seems to be that everyone connected with TM more or less constantly smiles). The outer office is for secretarial chores and is also used by a force of volunteer workers and teachers. The telephone is constantly ringing, most often to be answered with, "The first lecture is held Tuesday night at 8 P.M. No it doesn't cost anything. Twenty-three Cornelia Street is right off Avenue of the Americas."

More than five thousand people walked into this building for the first time last year. Most visitors came because friends had convinced them that there was indeed something of substance to transcendental meditation, and they were curious enough to want to investigate on their own.

Before anyone can be initiated (and given the technique) they must attend two lectures that outline exactly what TM is all about. The lectures are usually given at the center although, more and more, first lectures are conducted in an established meditator's living room. The instructors at all lectures are always Maharishi-trained TM teachers. The first lecture deals with "The Vision of Possibilities," or what an individual can accomplish with the help of meditation. The second lecture is more specific and deals with the mechanics of the technique.

At the New York City center the lectures are given in a large assembly room. Before the lecture begins the thirty to forty people who usually attend are asked to wait in a small, curtained-off anteroom. The room is neatly and comfortably furnished with vinyl-covered couches and chairs. A bulletin board is filled with the latest TM newsletters from across the country, as well as advertisements with a TM twist: "Wanted—meditator roommate for 2-bedroom apartment." "Meditator wants ride to California." "Meditator director wants TM-oriented play."

There is also a large piece of clouded white glass, lit from behind, imbedded in one wall. The rear light makes it possible to see the color transparencies someone has taped to the glass. They are recent photographs of the Maharishi. The view in each one is similar; a small, full-bearded, dhoti-wearing, smiling man, surrounded by flowers.

The curtain that separates this anteroom from the rest of the assembly room is pulled back to reveal a long, rectangular room. At the far end, perhaps twenty yards away, are two much smaller rooms. These rooms, meditation rooms, extend about ten feet from the back wall and are perhaps six feet in width. Along each wall are folded walls that roll out to form small open chambers for private meditation. The rear wall between the meditation rooms is a combination of glass and brick. Through the glass a brick wall of another building is visible. The area between the two buildings has been turned into a lighted garden. On the brick wall inside this room is a painting of the Maharishi's old and departed teacher. Just in front of this painting is a small vase with a single flower. The room looks wonderfully warm.

Gray folding chairs, set up assembly style, face a small platform on which two more chairs face the room. "What we'd like to do tonight," one of the female teachers begins, "is to cover a vision of possibilities, in terms of the individual, in terms of the expansion of one's mental potential and bettering one's health. Then we'd like to make the vision a little larger and expand into the possibilities this might have in terms of society and bringing about permanent world peace."

The listeners are a cross-section of society. Al-

41

though there are usually more young people than old, both groups are solidly represented. The younger people dress casually, while it is obvious the older people have prepared themselves for the meetings, at least sartorially, with ties and jackets for the men and neat dresses for the women. There is only an occasional Black, a problem that the movement admits and is trying hard to solve.

During the lectures, there is rarely much sound or movement, but as the speaker goes on there is some slight fidgeting. Later discussions reveal that many of the people who attend the lectures have already decided to go ahead and be initiated. They don't pay a great deal of attention to the philosophy of the movement, especially since the first lecture tends to be quite complex for someone who lacks all understanding of meditation.

Many of the people who did not have their minds made up when they attended the first lecture decide to begin solely because of the congeniality of the people they meet at the center. Most centers report that more than two-thirds of the people who attend the initial lecture eventually come back for the second lecture; of that number, most are eventually initiated.

"I think what I'm really going to talk about," the speaker begins, "is about a tree, and about nature. One day we notice that something is wrong with the tree. The fruit isn't blossoming as . . ." The lecture ends seventy minutes later with a brief discussion of the possibilities of world peace through TM. From the limited number of questions it appears that much of the lecture was above the heads of the listeners. At its conclusion small groups cluster about trying to decipher what they've just heard. Most people wait until the second lecture before announcing their decision to be initiated. In other branches of TM, the Spiritual Regeneration Movement for example, the two lectures are combined into a single talk.

Near the conclusion of the second lecture there is a much more spirited question-and-answer period than at the first meeting. This time skeptics have obviously been listening carefully, trying to catch the speaker in a contradiction. When they feel they have, they pounce on it and challenge the lecturer.

After the completion of the second lecture, appointments are made by those who want to be initiated. If an individual has been using drugs he is asked to wait fifteen days. Others are told to bring three pieces of sweet fruit, at least six fresh flowers, and a clean handkerchief to the initiation ceremony.*

One skeptical recruit who heard both lectures and decided to become a meditator is Curtis Phillips. He is a thirty-six-year-old attorney who was born in North Carolina. He was married shortly after he turned twenty. The marriage was annulled and his former wife remarried. Later this year he expects to marry an extremely pretty woman who writes advertising copy.

Several years ago, Phillips tried analysis but gave

---

* Of everything an individual does in TM, this practice seems the strangest. Actually, the fruit, flowers, and handkerchief have no practical use. They are a traditional part of the ceremony, and are to TM what white wigs are to English barristers. These accouterments take on no magical properties. After the ceremony one flower, one piece of fruit, and the handkerchief are returned to the initiate if he desires. But most people refuse to take them away, and so the centers are well supplied with mums, tulips, and roses, and meditators are constantly being offered apples, pears, and peaches.

it up after twenty months. "It seemed futile," he told us. "I felt that I had tried long enough to get some results, and when I didn't get any I just got off the couch."

He maintains that TM helped solve most of his problems, which were:

1. "I had this haunting fear of being disapproved of. When a woman would tell me that I was great and that she loved me, I was sure she was lying."
2. "Down deep, I knew that my former wife had contributed heavily to our breakup, but I kept thinking that it was all my fault."
3. "Although I did a great deal of the work, I would deliberately let my law partners get all the glory—and then I'd complain about it."
4. "I always had this feeling of inferiority and would continuously belittle myself—try to make a good impression or defend an opinion."
5. "At four P.M., or even earlier, I'd get so tired that I would literally have to drag myself through the rest of the day. Twice I fell asleep during a trial in court. More and more, I resorted to pep pills."

Phillips is not a joiner and at first was reluctant to undertake TM. However he did and at the request of the authors Phillips kept a detailed diary of his thoughts and experiences upon becoming a meditator. They were very complete and after reading his notes and comparing them with what we had heard from others, we found that his experiences with transcendental meditation were quite typical. His diary follows in full.

I approached 23 Cornelia Street with an apple, a pear, and a persimmon, nine mums, a brand-new white handkerchief, a great deal of apprehension, and a dash of skepticism. There were many reasons why I had decided to become a meditator, but the final push had come from friends. By the time I got around to attending the lectures I had more or less decided I would be initiated.

I felt a bit shy and perhaps a bit foolish as I walked into the center holding my sweet fruit, flowers, and kerchief. I had been instructed that they were required for the initiation ceremony. I thought it was a lot of nonsense but I did as I was told. I wondered what lay in store: was I about to climb a peak or perhaps fall off a cliff? Was this to be the end of one life style and the beginning of another? What was behind that door with the picture of the Maharishi on it?

A lot of smiling faces, first of all. There seemed to be a great deal of excitement among the teachers, directed more to the new initiates than themselves. I walked into the office and sat down. I had been told that the entire initiation process would take approximately an hour and a half. I had arrived a little after three, early for my three-thirty appointment.

The first thing I did was fill out the usual membership card: name, address, and phone number, all those ciphers that make differences between people. I was then asked to sit in the small room I had waited in before when I'd attended the lectures. As I walked into the room, the first thing I smelled was sweet incense, and I was half-convinced that I had stepped into some kind of phony Eastern cult.

I settled into a sofa and tried to look as inconspicuous as possible. I was very careful about not drawing any attention to myself. There were only two other people in the room. They had their shoes off. Although no one told me to, it seemed the thing to do and so I removed mine.

The three of us sat there avoiding each other's eyes for perhaps fifteen minutes. Finally an SIMS official came into the room and began making out a receipt for the check I had yet to give him. "Are you a student?" he asked. I could have said yes and saved $40, and I have no doubts he would have believed me, but instead I made out the check for $75. He left and returned shortly with my fruit, flowers, and handkerchief, now arranged neatly in a small wicker basket. There were seven similar baskets lying on a table nearby. As time passed, the incense scent disappeared. Finally a young lady appeared and, with a smile, summoned one of the other two people. A short time later, the second person was also called.

Alone, I twiddled my thumbs. I could feel myself becoming quite nervous—no reason why I should, but I was. I thought back on the earlier initiations of my life: the Cub Scouts, Boy Scouts, the Army Reserves, and the first time I registered to vote. Life, it seemed to me right at that moment, is a series of initiations, each remarkably similar, but each to be faced with the same amount of discontent. Finally, my teacher walked into the room, picked up my basket and asked me to follow her.

We walked through the second, larger room and into the much smaller initiation room at the far end. This room had a large window that looked out on a lighted brick wall, making for a very soft effect. Sticks of incense burned and the room was lighted by a candle. In some way it reminded me of many of the apartments I had visited when I was in college. I suppose because it was closed off from the rest of the building and had its own heater. There were two chairs and a table in the room. The candle and the incense were on the table and over the candle was a painting of the Maharishi's teacher.

My teacher briefly explained to me what the ceremony consisted of.* Then we both stood in front of the portrait and she sang, quite softly, some lilting sentences in Sanskrit. The fruit, flowers, and handkerchief I had brought were used as symbolic offerings to Maharishi's teacher, the Guru Dev. The flowers were representative of life, the fruit the seed of life, and the handkerchief the cleansing of the spirit. The ceremony, I discovered, had little to do with the individual initiate. It seemed more to remind the instructor that this method he or she is passing on is not their own, but rather has been given to them by the Maharishi.

After concluding the chanting, which included the names of many of the "masters" who have kept the technique intact for thousands of years, my instructor turned to me and asked me to repeat a two-syllable word after her. This was to be my mantra.

By dictionary definition, a mantra is a "sacred counsel, formula, a mystical formula of invocation or incantation in Hinduism or Mahayana Buddhism." Each individual's mantra is considered to be his own property, the only thing that is never to be shared with anyone else.

---

* "The actual ceremony lasted less than a half hour," remembered another meditator, a Connecticut druggist. "Although at the time I understood little of what was being said, it was very pleasant." The ceremony has a two-fold purpose. It serves to impress upon the initiate that he is following an ancient tradition, and to remind the teacher that he is only handing down what he himself has been taught.

There is evidently a limited list of mantras, because it was explained at one of the lectures that more than one person can have the same mantra. We had been told that every individual had a mantra especially selected for him. I doubted that when I first heard it and, upon being given my mantra, continued to doubt it.

My mantra seemed harsh, a bit grating and, at first, somewhat hard to pronounce. I considered asking for a different mantra, one I felt more comfortable with, one with softer tones, but I decided not to.

My instructor asked me to repeat it over and over. I did, at times mispronouncing it, other times almost forgetting it. After I used a number of pronunciations she asked me to say it softer, then softer. Finally she told me to close my eyes and repeat it to myself without moving my tongue or my lips. "Don't worry if it starts to slip away," she said. "Let it."

I did. The first thing I saw when I closed my eyes was my mantra, *in huge, neon-lit letters*. It seemed to flash on and off. Finally it literally began fading away, getting smaller and smaller. More signs, all saying the same two-syllable word, appeared and I began to think that I was watching a television commercial for transcendental meditation.

Before I realized it, I was meditating. It was incredible. My very first taste of this "thing" that so many people had been trying to describe to me. I actually felt a wave of relaxation, an entirely physical feeling, sweep through my entire body. Then I thought "Is this it? Is this worth $75?"

Suddenly I heard someone hammering. (Outside, some telephone repair men were digging.) It brought me much closer to total consciousness but, almost on command, my mantra reappeared in my mind. My

teacher finally asked me to open my eyes very slowly,
so as not to jar my system awake all at once.

We discussed these first feelings. My relaxation,
my first brief thoughts. Besides the neon-lit mantra
I had seen waves of colors sliding formlessly by and
seemed to recall a record I had played the previous
night, Mozart's "Requiem." I closed my eyes again
and began repeating my mantra. The first car I ever
owned, a 1948 Ford, came into view, for some reason.
I have no idea why my mind picked this moment to
pop this car off my mental toaster. It didn't last long
and was replaced by memories of the one o'clock
movie I had watched the night before entitled, "Mon-
ster From The Surf." But that was gone almost as
soon as it arrived.

I began to realize that I was indeed meditating
and the specific thoughts began to fade. I just began
to enjoy the sense of total relaxation that I felt.

Finally: "Open your eyes, very slowly," my
teacher warned. We stood up and walked outside.
She asked me to sit down behind one of the moveable
walls and meditate. She told me that someone would
tell me when to cease meditating.* When that happened I was to make sure I took my time opening my
eyes, two or three minutes if necessary, before rising.

I sat down and stared into the wall. Slowly, I
closed my eyes and began to repeat my mantra, over
and over. This little nook lacked the warmth of the
room I was initiated in and wasn't quite as soundless.
I began to hear the noises around me. I "felt" it when
someone turned on the overhead light.

I began to realize that the act of meditation is a

---

* This is usually a brief period—no more than fifteen minutes—that enables the new meditator to practice what he has
just learned.

cycle: You start slowly and get deeper and deeper until you reach a fixed point, and then the upward journey begins. I was quite sure that I had reached bottom in the other room, or at least as deep as I could go with no meditation experience; at one point *I lost all sense of balance and thought I was going to fall right out of the chair. I suddenly felt nauseous.* We had been warned not to eat anything heavy before arriving at the center, but I had thrown down a quick sandwich. Now it was having its effect. I tried to put it out of my mind. I imagined myself picking up the feeling of nausea out of my stomach and placing it on the side, to be forgotten. And, for the most part, it was.

*I became very irritated at each sound.** I wanted to concentrate on my meditation, a contradiction in terms as I later found out. The thing about meditation is not to concentrate, but to take the reins off your mind and let it run anywhere it wants. But I realized that now I must be reaching the end of my meditation cycle because I felt totally awake, I had to fight to keep my eyes closed. Finally a male voice said, "Please open your eyes now."

I remembered my instructions, to take my time to open my eyes, and it was a good thing that I did. I was a lot deeper into meditation than I realized. The light, the voices, the feeling of being awake, all came as great surprises. I felt as if I had been sitting on the end of a high diving board while thinking I was actually on the edge of the pool: The water was a lot further away than I would have believed. I

---

* This is a problem most new meditators experience and is almost unavoidable. The longer you meditate, however, the easier it becomes to accept outside sounds without being irritated.

slowly got up and, taking a moment to regain my sense of balance, walked into the anteroom.

I was given a simple answer sheet and asked to fill it out. After listing my name and age I moved to the first question: "How long did you meditate?" I was stumped. I didn't realize it, but I had lost all track of time. The answer, I learned later, was twenty-two minutes, a good time period for a single meditation. The second question was, "How do you feel now in mind and body?" I put down what I'm sure thousands before me had answered: "Refreshed, and like I've touched onto something quite different from anything I've ever experienced."

"*Was it easy?* Yes."

"*Was it peaceful?* Yes."

"*Was there any moment of pleasantness?* Yes."

"*Did you at any moment feel sleepy during meditation?* Yes."

"*Do you feel sleepy now, after meditation?* No."

"*Did the mantra change in any way—did you feel that at times it became slower or faster or fainter?* At times it totally disappeared."

"*Did you sometimes lose the mantra?* Yes."

"*Did many thoughts come to you?* Yes."

"*Did thoughts disturb you?* Some."

"*Did you hear outside noises?* Yes."

"*Did you feel disturbed by outer noise?* Yes."

I was told that the best times to meditate were after waking fully but before breakfast and, at night, before dinner. My stomach was still churning, so I didn't have to ask why. I asked about the other things that had been in the room, the candle, the incense, the warmth of the room. During my meditation I thought that the perfect place to meditate would be in front of a fireplace, the most comfortable place I could think of. I was wrong.

"You can meditate in an automobile," my teacher said. "Naturally not when you're doing the driving." The candle, the incense, and the warmth—just like the flowers, the fruit, and handkerchief—are all traditional parts of the ceremony, but not necessary for meditation. Finally we returned to the office. I put my coat on and left.

I did not start seeing things differently outside. I had not discovered an entire new perspective on life. But I did have real feelings of wonderment, perhaps surprise, as I walked down Sixth Avenue. I was now a meditator.

I meditated by myself, at home, about three hours later. As my teacher had suggested, I used no candles, incense, or soft music. I sat myself down on the corner of my couch and began saying my mantra over and over in my mind. I have to admit I felt quite foolish doing it—until I began to sink further and further into my mind and quite forgot to feel foolish. This time I have far fewer memories about my meditation. I can remember worrying that the phone would ring and disturb me—a usual occurrence in my apartment. I wondered what I would do if it did, and decided I would probably just let it ring. In our lectures we had been told some of the problems we might have during meditation: everything from a baby crying to the neighbors fighting. The antidote was to let your mind float free. My particular problem was my cat. As soon as I sat down he hopped up on my lap, but strangely it didn't disturb my meditation at all.

My teacher had explained that I should meditate for twenty minutes and I set the alarm clock in my radio. She had warned me that the jarring effect of the alarm going off would be harsh, but I kept it low and turned it to a station I knew would be playing music. Actually it worked quite well. When I first started coming out of the meditation I simply wasn't sure I hadn't fallen asleep. I had the same bitter taste in my mouth that I often wake up with. I had few memories of my meditation, certainly none compared to those I had had in the SIMS center. But the fact that I was so totally awake so quickly convinced me I hadn't been sleeping. Normally, because I am a very deep sleeper, it takes me up to twenty minutes just to awaken fully. I was wide awake thirty seconds after I opened my eyes.

Thoughts began coming back to me. I remember thinking how terribly comfortable I was. I remember thinking that one major advantage meditation had over sleeping was that I could remember all my thoughts—and then I proceeded to forget them. And finally I remembered thinking, while deeply into meditation, about the taste in my mouth. It occurred to me that the solution would be to get up and get something to chew on. Otherwise, I felt fine and fully rested. I had a distinct feeling of excitement. Although I have heard very little about possible after effects, *I did feel just the slightest bit dizzy. But the dizziness soon disappeared.*

Later that first night I began to reflect on the experiences of the day. TM had certainly been more comfortable, and easy to get into, than I had originally thought. As I was thinking about TM, I realized one very important thing: I had totally forgotten my mantra. It was completely gone. I tried to recreate

the moment I had been given the word, but still it
wouldn't come. Finally, slowly, it began to come
back, until I was finally sure that I had recovered it.
My method of recalling it was simple: it sounds like
a friend's wife's first name.

Second Meditation

I woke this morning, believe it or not, with my
mantra on my mind. It didn't seem quite the same
as the one I had remembered the night before, but I
knew it was the correct word. I quickly washed until
I felt totally awake, and, taking the precaution of
letting my cat onto the fire escape, sat down to meditate. I was determined to discover if I had indeed
fallen asleep while meditating last night. I wasn't
going to set the clock. If I "finished" in an hour-plus
I would know I had been sleeping.

Again, as I began saying my mantra, *I felt very
foolish*. I wondered if I would have had the courage
to say it aloud with someone else in the room. I
wondered if I would ever even meditate with someone else in the room. It seemed to take a little longer
to reach the same point of relaxation I had experienced yesterday. Perhaps I was too conscious of the
questions I was asking myself: *Am I really meditating? Is my respiratory rate slowing down? Am I doing
it properly?*

I could feel the cycle deepening. I began to won-
der what time it was, how long I had been under. Five
minutes? An hour? I remembered that my instructor
had said not to be afraid to sneak a look at the clock.
I did. Twelve minutes had passed. Back to my mantra.

A few distractions: my cat returned and wanted
his head scratched and the back of my neck started

itching. I ignored the cat, but it wasn't easy to ignore the itch. I finally had to give in, and when I did, I seemed to lose my place in the cycle. But I quickly returned to my mantra and dove back in. More time passed. Check the clock. Eighteen minutes. Did I sleep for a few seconds? Twenty-two minutes. I slowly, very slowly, opened my eyes. At first I thought my meditation was not as successful as it had been the night before, but then, as I began putting these words down, I realized what a separate and distinct experience it had been. This time, I am positive, I was awake the entire period, but I have so little memory of my thoughts. At two o'clock today, at the meeting of the new initiates, I'll find out if my experiences were standard or unusual.

This was probably the frankest session I attended. I arrived for the post-initiation instruction just a little after 2 P.M. and found five other new initiates sitting in the waiting room. All were new faces, so I guess I was one of the first people from the two lectures I attended actually to become an initiate. One of the group was a very distinguished-looking man. He had bright silver hair and a striking goatee and wore a professorial green tweed sports jacket. Another participant was a matronly woman who appeared to be in her mid-fifties.

While we waited for the teacher to arrive we filled out a second answer sheet. It was similar to the one we had filled out yesterday:

"*How many times have you meditated since your last checking?* Twice."

"*How long did you meditate each time?* Twenty minutes."

"Did you feel that the time during meditation passed quickly? Yes."

"Did you at any moment find that you were unaware of body and surroundings? Yes."

"Did you at moments feel some happiness within? Yes."

"Did thoughts disturb you? No."

"During meditation did you notice any change in breathing? Yes."

"During meditation did you feel so relaxed as to feel sleepy? No."

"How do you feel today compared with other days? Fine."

"Are you satisfied with meditation so far? Yes."

"Any other remarks? Blank."

We moved into the meeting room. Six chairs had been arranged in a semicircle around a seventh. Our instructor took the odd chair. She smiled at us.

"Well?" she asked.

No one answered immediately. She broke the silence by reemphasizing the fact that although meditation in itself is a pleasurable act, we don't meditate for the physical feeling. The reason we meditate, she explained, is to make our active lives more fulfilling. To have more energy, be more alive. She asked for our reactions and I immediately discovered that my experiences had not been unusual.

"I think I fell asleep," one of the men said.

I added that I thought I might have, too, but I wasn't sure.

"How did you know you were asleep?" she asked.

Neither of us could really answer and she asked if we had been awake after twenty minutes. He said he had, and I confessed that I had cheated and used my alarm clock.

According to her definition, neither of us had slept, because we both awoke completely conscious rather than in that stupor that usually accompanies being awakened from a short nap. Secondly, both of us maintained our sitting positions, rather than slumping to one side as is normal when an individual falls asleep sitting up. What had probably happened, she said, was that we had touched base deeply, more deeply than conscious thought, and since it is the feeling we most closely associate with sleep—simply because we know no other feeling like it—we call it sleep.

"If you are meditating and you get so tired you can't even keep your head up," she said, smiling, "then put your head down and go to sleep. When you wake, meditate for five or ten minutes and then slowly open your eyes."

"How would you know if you were meditating wrong?" someone asked.

"You'd *feel* it," she said. "Meditation, as we've so often heard, differs from concentration and contemplation in that there are no restraints on your mind. It is left to wander."

She compared concentrating with our minds to trying to stop a car with our hands—we'd feel it. In this case there would be pressure on the forehead, very light and not lasting very long, just enough to indicate we were pushing and pulling rather than "just going along wherever your mind decides to take you."

"I got terribly afraid I was going to forget my mantra," one of the students said.

I chimed in again, "I forgot mine."

Again, we were told that this was a perfectly normal reaction. Being new and unusual sounds, our mantras took some getting used to. And, more important, we associated them with a certain state of mind. When our mind was busy with other thoughts, on a different level, we forgot the mantra—a very common experience.

I said that this morning, just as I was ready to meditate, my mantra reappeared.

"Don't go around repeating your mantra," she warned, "because when you are walking around you're on a different level of consciousness. Think of it this way: after you plant a seed, you don't continually dig it up just to make sure it's still there. You just let it stay in the ground and spread roots.

"For similar reasons," she continued, "*a mantra is not a magic spell* to be called when needed, for example when you've just missed a subway train or are caught in Sunday traffic. And, if during the day your mantra should pop into your head, it should be like a friendly, but unwanted guest. Just say 'hello' and then close the door."

The questions continued on that level until, suddenly, one of the men asked whether TM had any effect on sex. There was some nervous tittering among the students and I think I was the worst offender. For some reason I felt very embarrassed. The teacher, however, didn't seem to mind the question and started answering immediately.

"Yes, it can and often does," she replied. "Although the Maharishi himself is celibate, he does not advocate celibacy by other meditators. There are many case histories that lead to the conclusion that TM will improve an individual's sex life."*

---

* Although there have been no scientific surveys concerning TM and sex, we heard of numerous couples whose sexual relations greatly benefited through meditation.

She told the group of a typical case. The woman was a thirty-four-year-old school teacher and had one child. She complained that sex was never satisfying. After the birth of the child she always pretended to be indisposed and thus avoided normal sexual relations.

I was fascinated by the story. I guess the entire class was, but I must admit that there was nothing salacious in the way it was being related.

Anyway, the woman and her husband were pretty desperate about the situation and finally went to their minister seeking help. He suggested they attend the clinic of Masters and Johnson, the authors of *Human Sexual Inadequacy.* They agreed to, but decided at the last minute to try transcendental meditation before contacting Masters and Johnson.

"I guess they gave TM a chance because it was cheaper," said the teacher with a laugh. "TM worked. Tension and guilt seemed to be behind their sexual troubles. I think we often look for very complicated reasons but in reality the reasons may be quite simple. In this case, as in many cases, the couple was surrounded by stress and strain that made it impossible to perform properly in bed. This was all compounded by the guilt they felt about the actual sex act. After a period of meditating they began liking themselves and in turn started liking each other. Tension evaporated. Nothing complicated or involved in the solution!

"Generally, cases like that work out for the better. A person's sex life tends to become healthy as his mind becomes healthy. If he has been afraid of going near people, very often that fear will disappear. If he has a hang-up that has been ruining his sex life, chances are that hang-up will also disappear. During

TM there is usually a great deal of improvement in one's physical, emotional, and intellectual conditions. As I've said previously, 'You simply become nicer to yourself!' "

She paused after making the last statement as if to see if there were any more questions concerning sex. There weren't.

"Did any of you notice a difference between your meditation last night and this morning?" she asked.

The matronly woman in our group spoke up: "It was not as deep this morning as it was last night."

"When we meditate at night," the instructor explained, "our bodies are tired. In the morning we've already had a full night's rest."

The questions and answers continued. Did anyone notice more proficiency in anything? A young man said he did. He thought he had done a calculus problem much more easily than he had the week before. *I really couldn't accept that, but I didn't say anything.*

We moved onto more practical matters—my cat, among other things. Cats and dogs and little children and ringing telephones and incessant visitors were quite typical problems. Since it is best for the new meditator to seek quiet, if possible, a cat or a dog should be locked up somewhere during meditation. Little children aren't handled so easily, but if it's at all possible some provision should be made to be out of their sight—for example locking yourself in the bathroom. As for the phone—off the hook. And visitors, well, answer the door and, when they finally leave, finish meditating.

A final question: *"Did anyone feel itchy?"*

I said I did. She didn't seem surprised and asked what I did about it. "I thought about it for awhile," I said, "then I scratched it." Exactly what I was supposed to do, it seems. *Being comfortable is the most important thing,* and if you're cold, or itching, or fidgety, it's impossible to be comfortable.

There were no more questions. As as group, we now closed our eyes for half a minute. Open. Closed them again. And opened them again. Finally we meditated as a group. I had very little trouble getting deeply into meditation this time. I thought I was aware of the sounds around me, but managed to keep some of them out. To make sure that I wasn't sleeping, I kept up a lively conversation with myself. I continually told myself to relax, that I was in the middle of a meditation period and I was not sleeping. I can remember saying that over and over.* Finally, after a period of time (I can't honestly say how long) our teacher said, "Open your eyes very slowly." I hadn't realized how far away I was. The only physical thing I can now remember is being annoyed when someone worked at a typewriter in the outer room.

"Did anyone hear that dog barking except me?" the "professor" on my left asked.

I thought he was kidding, but it seems I was the only one who hadn't heard it! There really was a dog, and it was really barking, and I really didn't hear it. I must have been much deeper into meditation than I realized. So much for that lesson.

Fifth Meditation

. . . decided to concentrate on meditating for twenty minutes without relying on the clock. But in

---

* By telling himself to relax and consciously preventing himself from sleeping, Phillips was doing two things wrong. It is not necessary to remind yourself to relax; the soothing sound of the mantra automatically helps to relax you. And there is absolutely nothing wrong with falling asleep during meditation. In fact, if you're that tired, you should go to sleep and resume your meditation when you awaken.

my mind I saw a clock. It reappeared after what felt like ten minutes and again after fifteen minutes. When I thought twenty minutes were up, I finally opened my eyes. It had been exactly twenty minutes!

Sixth Meditation

. . . many strange memories popped into my mind during this meditation. I remembered being on active duty in the army and getting caught sleeping under my bed . . .*

Third Day

I have never seen anyone who smiles as much as our teacher. A wide, warm smile full of friendliness. A happy person. Even when her eyes are closed as she meditates, her constant smile is there.**

We filled out another form today, a different color but the questions were very much the same. There were a few new ones:

"*Approximately how many times did you lose the mantra during meditation?* Often."

---

* There is no limit to the range of what you may remember during meditation. A Pennsylvania librarian recalled the very pleasant highlights of her high-school senior prom; a New York plant manager vividly remembered a clambake fifteen years earlier, at which "I had the best damn piece of corn on the cob I've ever eaten."

Thoughts have no real meaning in TM, although they are usually quite pleasant. When a meditator becomes aware that he is thinking, he simply returns to his mantra.

** We are aware of the possibly irritating ubiquity of smiling faces, but we were both struck by the vast number of truly happy, smiling meditators we met. And, unlike the pinned-on smiles of airline stewardesses or restaurant hostesses, the TM-induced happiness seemed genuine.

"Do you remember moments when there was no mantra and no thoughts? Yes."

"After meditation do you feel inclined to rest or do you feel energetic? Energetic."

"Have you noticed any indication of increasing clarity of mind? No."

"Have you noticed any improvement in your relationship with others? No."

"Has anyone remarked upon any change in you? No."

"How do you feel today as compared to yesterday? Fine."

"Do you now feel you have understood how to meditate? Yes."

Yes, I most certainly do. We were meeting this day in the basement of the SIMS center because the larger room was being used for a lecture. I sat down next to the older woman and began discussing the course. Like almost everyone else, she had come on someone else's recommendation, in this case her sister's.

"She's involved in so many different things," the woman remarked, "and when she told me she thought this would be good for me I thought I'd try it. She knows me so well."

The meeting began with questions. The man who looked like a professor had been meditating on the bus. He had been successful the first night. The second night he had unfortunately gotten a seat over the wheels and couldn't keep the sound of the bus out of his mind. He said it sounded like "Heinie Manush." It was a problem, our instructor agreed, but reminded us that even though it may seem as if we were not "into it," we probably were.

One of the other men had had the same problem

I did. The first night he had forgotten his mantra, and now, although he thought he had remembered it, he just wasn't sure it was precisely the right word. She said she would check it with him before we meditated. She did so, but in private.

Someone else brought up the problem of eating and meditating. The first day, I remembered, I had eaten a rather large meal and gotten an upset stomach, something I figured to be psychosomatic. It wasn't, and the explanation made a great deal of sense. When you meditate, all your body processes slow down, including digestion. If you've had a big meal, and are in the process of digestion, meditation would slow it up considerably, and thus cause minor cramps.

The best time to meditate, our teacher said, was about half an hour after a light snack, an hour after a small meal, and at least three hours after a large meal.

"It's better to have a small snack before breakfast, meditate, and then a late breakfast," someone suggested. She said laughingly that it might prove to be expensive, but it sounded like a good idea.

The "professor" asked about the importance of meditating at the same time every day.

"It doesn't have to be at exactly the same time," was the answer, "but it is good to keep somewhat regular hours. *If you wait until you're ready to go to bed before meditating, you probably won't be able to sleep all night.*"

Then she had a question of her own.

"Has anybody thought during their meditation that this is sure a waste of time, that they could be using the time for something better?"

There was a collective nodding of heads.

"That's fine," she smiled, "and most natural. Don't

worry about it, just go back to your mantra. Treat it as you would any other thought, say 'fine,' and return to the mantra."

There were a few more minor questions, ranging from the difference between *thinking* the mantra and *saying* it aloud, to the range of thoughts that ran through our minds. Then we meditated again. Once more I fell into it very easily. I felt like I was floating. Elapsed time (I had to ask): thirteen minutes.

The next step was a bit different. Evidently we had reached a point where we could understand what we were doing while we meditated. Smiling as usual, our instructor reached across a chair and turned on a tape recorder. This lesson, as it turned out, was to be taught by the Maharishi. I had once heard his voice described as a [thirty-three and one-third rpm. record being played at seventy-eight] but until this moment I didn't realize how accurate that description was. His voice was light and somewhat melodic. At times it was quite difficult to understand the point he was trying to make.

He began by explaining that every mental process of the body has a physical counterpart. When our minds work, our bodies work. Therefore, we want our minds to work in the most comfortable direction. He moved along and I lost him. I caught up with him when he started speaking about the thoughts we had during meditation. They are not to be worried about, he said, because they are not at all important in terms of content. A thought is only a symbol, he said, and its meaning (during meditation) is only that we must dive deep into our consciousness again. When we have thoughts during meditation it means we are operating on the surface and we are supposed to go below the surface. Accept the thought for what it is:

a message to dive again, a message that more stress has been released. The tape stopped.

Our teacher began trying to explain what the Maharishi had said. I followed her just a little better than I had the Maharishi. "Some thoughts may be nice," she told us, "others quite ugly, but they really make no difference at all. The thoughts themselves have absolutely no meaning, except that it is time to begin getting back to the mantra." Well, so much for my army memories.

One young man asked if there was a goal to all of this. There is, it turns out, but we have to wait until tomorrow to discover what it is. On the way out, I bumped into the man I had dubbed "professor" and asked him why he started meditating. "Because I was the only one in my family not doing it," he said.

His occupation, it turns out, was publishing. "TM got my kids off drugs, hard or soft, I'm not sure which, and I wanted to see if there was anything in it for me. I've been reading a book the Maharishi wrote, *The Science of Being and the Art of Living,* and I've seen an awful lot of parallels between TM and the Catholic upbringing I had. I told that to my son and he explained that TM existed two thousand years before Christ. I agreed with him, and said that Christ really wasn't teaching anything new, he was just doing it better than anyone else. It's the first thing we agreed on in a long time."

I walked on.

Eighth Meditation

. . . learned something else: they weren't kidding when they said to take the phone off the hook. I was in the middle of my meditation when it began ringing. It BLASTED me into wakefulness. Without a second thought I opened my eyes and started to get up. Whew! I quickly sat down for a few seconds and then answered the phone. I was in a daze. I couldn't talk. I finally went back to the meditation, but it was no good. Butterflies were flying all over my stomach. From now on the phone comes off the hook!

Ninth Meditation

. . . first real bad experience. As soon as I got into it, my stomach started churning, perhaps a remnant of last night. It lasted almost the entire time and proved very uncomfortable. For some reason I kept thinking of an aunt of mine who once told me that she had eaten three dinners.

Fourth Meeting

I had thought I was an official meditator before, but today I graduated from initiate to meditator. We filled out another form, gold this time, and quite similar to the others.

"*Have you noticed any effects from morning meditation continue through the day? No.*"

"*Have you realized that regular meditation, twice a day, is essential to stabilize benefits and sustain progress? Yes.*"

"*Do you appreciate the importance of regular checking? Yes.*"

We quickly moved to questions and answers. A young man in a blue sweater said he hadn't felt like meditating the night before, but had forced himself to do it and hence didn't feel he was getting anything out of it.

This was most natural, we were told. "And those are the most important times to meditate because there is obviously a reason you don't want to meditate, something causing stress in your system. And it is to relieve that stress that you're meditating in the first place."

I asked about my butterflies. The result of stress release. During meditation, the body releases stress. It usually happens rather slowly and gently, but sometimes it takes the form of a churning stomach. Since I hadn't accepted the fact that one shouldn't eat before meditating, I got an upset stomach. I decided to accept the teacher's explanation.

She asked if any of us thought we were still wasting our time. One person did. The thought came to him *during* meditation.

"Treat it as you would any other thought," she said. "It is just a message to return to the mantra."

She then wanted to know if anyone had had any results thus far, and a young man said he had. The night before he had been in a social situation in which he usually froze up. Last night he didn't. "Instead of being afraid to open my mouth," he said, "I started to make conversation. I even told a joke. People laughed, so I guess it was a funny one."

No one else reported drastic changes. "Most people don't notice results immediately," she said. "As a matter of fact, it's usually the people around you that notice things first." She went on to explain that, for some reason, age had something to do with it. The older you are, the longer it takes to get substantial results. Younger children seem to get the most the fastest. Then we meditated again. This time for twelve minutes.

The lecture subject for the day was the final major point, the goal of transcendental meditation. In the instructor's words it was very simple: "to lead a fuller life." But when she began explaining this "fuller life," matters became a little complicated.

Normally, she said, we live on three levels of consciousness: waking, sleeping, and dreaming. Each is an easily defined state and has a physiological counterpart. A scientist can tell what conscious state an individual is in by doing a simple physical examination. A fourth state of consciousness, the state that transcendental meditation brings us into, is called transcendental consciousness. Again, it has a physiological counterpart, and again a scientist or doctor could determine it with a short examination. There is also a fifth state, a state that encompasses all the other four states, the name of the goal in the Maharishi's terms: cosmic consciousness.

CC, as it is known, also has its physiological counterpart. It is cosmic consciousness that we are aiming at, that mode of life that enables us to "lead a fuller life." Exactly what it is, how one feels (better, obviously) our teacher did not explain. Some of it sounded like double talk. "Cosmic consciousness" evidently is often bandied about by veteran meditators in terms of how close one can get to it, and how long it takes.

How to get there? Meditate, son, meditate. After meditating for a minimum of eighteen months there are some advanced techniques that evidently help you get there much quicker and more easily.

Finally, our teacher rose and asked to speak to each person privately. When my turn came we returned to the initation room and sat down. She asked me to whisper my mantra, which I did, reminded me to come back in two weeks to be checked, and sent me on my way. I was now a full-fledged meditator.

Ten months have elapsed since I first started meditating. I don't want to sound technical, but my nervous system is better, I seem to have a broader base of understanding, my awareness of most subjects is more profound. I could go on and on, but I'll simply close by saying, "I feel a whole lot happier!"

5

People Who Meditate

The men, women, and children whose stories you are about to read are real. We met, interviewed, and were impressed by them. They are good people. But as one of them cautioned, "I don't think you would have liked me before I started meditating."

Because most of these case histories are of such a personal nature, we decided not to list names. There is one exception. Major General Franklin M. Davis is so easily identifiable that it would have been pointless to try to camouflage his identity. In all the other cases, names make little difference since they are so representative of similar stories heard daily in TM centers around the country.

"The Family That Meditates Together . . ."

Forty-year-old F.L. is the manager of a food company in a suburb of New York. He, his wife, and teen-aged daughter are an extremely attractive threesome and are very, very close.

"Not repulsively close," explains his wife, "but we're not ashamed to show that we like each other and that we enjoy doing things together."

They weren't always that way. In fact, a year and a half ago they were going in three different directions. But that's all part of the past. They credit the dramatic change to transcendental meditation. Let them tell you about it:

MR. F.L.—FATHER

You've heard the phrase about carrying two fifty-pound weights on your shoulders. Well I felt I was lugging around two one-hundred pound weights! I'd growl at the people in the plant and say they weren't working fast enough. When I answered the phone I'd snap at the caller. I'd even grumble at my boss and disagree with all his instructions. When the working day was over I'd get in my car to drive home. But a few minutes later I'd want to turn back.

If the car in front of me was doing less than fifty, I'd shake my fist and swear at the driver. When I got to my house I barely nodded at my wife. Instead, I'd reach for the bottle of scotch. Our daughter was never home and I'd shout, "Can't you keep her home?"

Before my wife could reply, I'd start arguing. It seemed that we argued all the time. We'd fight about ridiculous things like the chair not being in the right place or the garbage pail not lined properly. When our daughter came home, I'd shout at her, too.

Let's face it—I wasn't the easiest person to live with!

By nature I guess I'm a pretty skeptical person. I've always questioned everything and take things with *two* grains of salt. When John Glenn orbited the earth I wasn't satisfied with the story in *The New York*

Times and wrote away to NASA seeking their explanation. I remember when I was a kid in school, the teachers would give our class some proven facts and I would still pepper them with dopey questions. Were they sore!

I grew up in a small town in Iowa and came east right after the Korean War. I was a supply sergeant in Fort Benning, Georgia. When I moved to New York I got a job with the company I'm still with. That's where I met my wife. I guess I did my work well because I kept getting promoted. I'm in charge of forty-seven employees now.

Well, one of the men in my division meditated and kept insisting that I should do the same. "You'll feel a thousand percent better," he kept telling me.

I dismissed his advice because I thought him to be some kind of nut who thinks everything looks good. He'd jump into something and then jump right out again. I told him that transcendental meditation was a bunch of hot air. But when his wife started meditating it was a different story. They live near us and we regarded her as the complete opposite of her husband. She was very level headed and never would get involved in anything kooky.

So I wasn't too surprised when my wife agreed to go down with me to the transcendental meditation center. But I was flabbergasted when our daughter said she would also tag along. It had been years since she did anything with us. I think the last time she accompanied us she was still wearing diapers.

Well, you can imagine that ride. As usual, I bawled out all the other drivers on the road. One guy pulled up alongside me and wanted to start a fight. My wife made me drive away. Then we got into some kind of snit. I don't even remember what it was all about. All I remember was that we had one lulu of a fight—nobody was talking to nobody!

When we finally got to the center I had trouble finding a parking spot, and I blamed it on the entire population of New York. My wife said I behaved as if I felt it was all some kind of plot aimed at me. I sure was in a foul mood when we went in.

There were about thirty people waiting to hear the lecture—all ages, sizes, and shapes. A young boy whose hair was down to his shoulders was sitting in the first row. I swear he was barefoot. I was immediately sorry I had come, but I noticed the man sitting next to him. He was middle-aged, wearing a vest, and had neatly combed gray hair. He looked like some kind of investment broker. Next to him was a pretty woman in her late twenties who was very well-dressed in some kind of pink suit. She was probably a school teacher or a librarian. I decided to stay.

What stood out was the looks on the faces of the people connected with the center. They were very intelligent and seemed so peaceful. So happy. They laughed at things I had forgotten to laugh at. I found myself envious.

It's not that they were smug, but still I wanted to trip them up. However, I couldn't—they didn't make any wild claims. Just the opposite. There was nothing to argue about. At the end of that preliminary lecture I read everything posted on the walls and picked up some literature. On the ride home I was quiet. I was thinking.

The next week we went back for the second preliminary lecture. We didn't discuss it much at home, but we were all ready to leave about an hour before we actually had to. This time the lecturer told us that she had just been robbed and important papers had been stolen. She was concerned, but she was still able to function—even smile. If it had happened to me, I'd have climbed up a wall. I was sure impressed. So impressed that I decided to learn how to meditate. I guess the girls felt the same way because they also arranged for instruction.

We had been told that learning to meditate was simple, but I didn't think it would be so easy. Would you believe that at the end of that first week tension seemed to disappear? It really did! Just evaporated. I never felt so mentally and physically good in my entire life.

I felt so good that I was worried about what was happening to me. It had been a long time since I had laughed out loud. But I did. Some guy in the plant told me a real funny story and I let him know I enjoyed it. Usually I'd sneer even if I thought it was funny.

A typist in my division brought over a letter for me to sign that contained about three mistakes. Ordinarily I'd have taken her head off, but this time I merely said, "Do it over, please—we all make errors." And then I smiled. I remember the incredulous look of her face. I couldn't believe it myself.

One of the bosses rants and raves about everything. Nothing seems to please him. Normally I'd go into his office prepared for a fight. This time I went in and said my piece loud and clear—but I found that I wasn't saying it in a belligerent tone. I sounded reasonable, and what's more—he agreed with me!

When it got time to leave I was eager to go home. Driving back I started to swear at a couple of guys who seemed to be creeping along, but I found myself smiling. Try to be angry when you're smiling! Last week I even got out of my car to help an old man change a tire.

My wife would always complain that I was an

incessant talker—that I spoke just for the sake of speaking. I'd spend hours talking about the pressures I was under. When I'd speak to my daughter, I'd say the same thing over and over and over. There were times I'd go on for hours at a stretch—both at the job and at home. Now I don't pretend that I have become completely silent, but I'll vouch that I speak less than half as much as I did before.

My drinking has been cut down to practically nothing. Alcohol just doesn't seem to matter to me now. When I used to go to a party I'd be the nearest guy to the bar. Now I can nurse one drink the entire evening.

Another thing I did was to gobble up aspirins— I took them as if they were peanuts. Maybe it was because of the tension I was under, but whatever the reason was I'd constantly have headaches and reach for the aspirin bottle. The headaches have stopped. I've had only one headache since I started meditating and that one lasted just a short time. I've heard that sometimes TM causes side effects like nausea and a ringing in the ears, but, honestly, none of that has happened to me or to anyone I know.

My most serious problem was the way I acted to my wife and daughter. I'd been married nineteen years, and at times I wondered why I stayed married. I won't say that I always contemplated divorce, but at times the thought would cross my mind. Nothing I did seemed to please my wife. She'd nag me about my drinking. To spite her, I'd drink more! She'd nag me about my talking. To spite her, I'd talk more! It was as if life together was one big brawl.

I'm pretty close to my mother. She moved near us after my father died and I'd invite her over for dinner every few weeks. I'm an only child. Anyway, my wife claimed that my mother would constantly pick—that everything we did in our house was wrong. If anyone answered back it would cause a battle royal.

Last Thanksgiving we invited my mother over as usual. And as usual, she started picking. But this time we didn't rise to the bait. When my mother had gone, my wife and I laughed over it.

I found my house was going to pot over the years. I hadn't done anything to maintain it. Now I seem to be doing things. I haven't become the greatest handyman, but last Sunday I raked the leaves. I cleaned out the gutters and the cellar. My daughter helped me with that.

The two of us had drifted far apart. We didn't talk to each other about anything. Wait, that isn't completely true. When she was around I'd lecture her, but I felt it was going in one ear and out the other one. Now we talk to each other and even go places together. She went with us to see a Met game. Last summer the three of us drove to the Grand Canyon—it was her idea!

A couple of weeks after I started meditating, one of the mechanics in the plant said, "For crying out loud, I go home at night all aggravated and worked up. You used to be that way, too. Now you come in the morning all smiles. When you leave you're still smiling. Now what in hell is the matter with you?" I started to tell him, but he wouldn't believe me.

I don't try to proselytize everybody I meet but I have to admit I've been talking up meditation in the office and the neighborhood. Three guys I work with are meditating and also two of our neighbors. More say they will.

When I'm asked what TM means to me I don't give a long philosophical answer. I simply say, "To me meditation means inner calm. It's a method I use to be totally at ease, at peace with myself and the world."

I don't want to sound like some TV soap commercial full of superlatives. But if I'm going to be honest and level I have to admit that transcendental meditation brought on lots of changes—changes for the better!

A.R.L.—MOTHER

The doctor told me I was coming apart at the seams and headed for a nervous breakdown. That probably sounds like the beginning of some true confession story, but it was happening to me. It was for real!

I knew that my husband meant well, but it was increasingly difficult to live with him. We were sharing the same house but we acted more like strangers. I was also very concerned about my daughter. I suppose these days it's difficult to raise a teen-ager without worrying about the drug scene. I don't mean to imply that she was constantly on drugs, but I knew she was using marijuana. Her friends also left much to be desired. I tried to talk to her, but she'd tell me to mind my own business. Our discussions always ended that way.

When my husband said he was going down to the transcendental meditation center I agreed to go along. I was desperate and willing to try anything.

That night the lecture was given by a girl in her mid-twenties, and I kept thinking that if she had put her hair up and wore more becoming clothes she'd be quite attractive. Anyway, she explained what TM was all about. What it can do for you. That people from four to eighty can learn to meditate. Things like that. My friend Mary was meditating and told me it was easy, but this sounded too good to be true.

I found the second lecture beautiful. So much so that I decided to sign up. Evidently my husband and daughter felt the same way. Well, the initiation was surprisingly simple—and exhilarating. When it was over I was given a blue sheet of paper with some questions. I remember some of them:

"Was meditating easy?" I answered, "Very easy!"

"Was it peaceful?" My reply was, "Yes, very much so!"

At the end of the paper they asked for other remarks about my meditation. I wrote, "I feel in excellent shape. I hope I feel this way tomorrow."

The next day I meditated twice—once in the morning and the second time before we went down to the center. Meditating seemed to be working fine, but I was worried. I had tried analysis briefly and remembered that I felt that it also worked at the beginning but the effects soon wore off. The psychiatrist warned me that it would be a long time before I could see the results. With TM, I seemed to see results right away. Now, I'm not saying that TM takes the place of going to a shrink, but for me it worked!

I was a heavy smoker—two and a half packs a day. That's dropped off to where now I no longer have the desire to smoke—I constantly forget to light a cigarette.

What really pleased me was my new relationship with my husband. I probably sound girlish, but it's as if we're on a second honeymoon. I see my husband through different eyes and I like what I see. He is more considerate and I think I now strike him the same way.

Our sex life has improved tremendously. I was

told the reason is that we're both now a lot less tense and our inhibitions have gone away. Whatever the explanation, I'm very grateful.

It amazes me to see so many improvements, but I'd be less than honest if I didn't list them. I get along lots better with my daughter these days. Three weeks ago she brought home a girl she knew. The girl had run away from her house and needed a place to stay. Normally I'd have hit the roof and called her parents or the police or something. This time I talked to the girl in reasonable fashion and also to my daughter. The girl decided to return home. I'm not trying to maintain that everybody lived happily ever after, but the point I'm trying to make is that I didn't go all to pieces. I was able to cope with the situation. My daughter even thanked me, and that in itself was startling!

I had this bad back for a long time and the pain would come and go—mostly come! I tried all kinds of remedies, but the pain remained. Well, within two weeks after I started meditating it was gone for good. Probably for the same reason our sex life has become better—less tension!

Not everything is peaches and cream. Since taking up TM I've become more adventurous in my cooking and my family has started to complain. Like tonight, I plan to serve a dish I just concocted—shrimp, apples, and avocadoes baked in wine sauce topped with whipped cream. It may sound indigestible, but there is one thing I can count on—the three of us will get upset stomachs together. Like they say: "The family that meditates together, radiates together!"

B.M.L.—DAUGHTER

I don't think my reasons for meditating were the same as my parents'. At first, TM to me was more like a game, something new I could play with. Let's say I blew hot and cold. There were times I thought it was the greatest thing in the world, but more often I felt it was just a silly bore. But when I started changing, I got really interested and came to love meditating. Maybe the best way I can describe my feelings is by telling you a typical recent day.

Mornings I'm usually a very slow starter. Any morning—but especially Monday. Well, last Monday I got up, washed and then meditated. I never used to eat breakfast, but now I do. And what's more, I eat it with my mother and father. Not just juice and coffee either. That morning I had a boiled egg, toast, farina and milk. Lucky for me, I'm not the kind that puts on weight.

I'm a senior and don't have to get to school the moment the bell rings, but any way I'm usually early. It was a warm, sunny day so I walked. I entered my homeroom about five minutes before starting time and I was all smiles. I was cheerful and really happy. The teacher said, "Wow, you must have had a great weekend!"

She knows that I meditate and I think that she'll start soon. She's not too young, I'd say about thirty-three or thirty-four, and doesn't have a boyfriend. Maybe TM will help her get one.

I'm the managing editor on the school newspaper and was immediately told by one of the other editors that we had a big problem—our adviser had censored a story and we had to get another one real quick.

Ordinarily I would have blown my cool, but this time I took the news real calm and said that I'd write a story during my study period. This other guy on the newspaper shook his head and said, "You're just not the same! Whatever it is, I want to buy several pounds!" I think he'll soon start meditating, too.

I did write the story during my study period and, if I say so myself, it was a good one. That, too, is something new. I never would have dared to compliment myself before.

I have four major subjects on Monday and I feel I did well in all of them. I participated in class and debated with the teachers—but not repulsively. I was unsure about a couple of things and asked questions instead of keeping mum and sweating over it at home or giving myself an excuse for not doing the assignment. My whole attitude toward school has changed. I guess my attitude toward everything else has also changed.

Prior to meditation I was always kind of searching. I felt depressed most of the time, not happy or satisfied with myself. If people said I was pretty—I guess I am—I just wouldn't believe it and accused them of lying. It was as if I didn't belong to anyone or anything, that I was going nowhere.

I used to smoke marijuana a couple of times a week and I've tried LSD and mescaline. Things like that. The desire for drugs has left me. With TM, life seems more fulfilling so you don't need the drug.

A friend of mine who was a steady user of marijuana is now also meditating—I was responsible for her initiation. Anyway, she is completely off drugs. I'm pretty close to her, but then I was always close to kids my own age. It was my parents that I had trouble with.

I don't want you to think I'm a cornball, but I'm enjoying my parents now. Really. We're much closer. That's a laugh because anything would be an improvement over the way we used to be. It got so that whenever I'd hear my mother or father call my name I'd know they were on the verge of bawling me out.

We fought all the time. That's the chief reason I stayed out of the house so much.

To be honest, I think my parents depend a little too much on meditation. They more or less pin everything down to TM. I more or less pin everything down to myself. But then I guess TM lets you be yourself . . . It's kind of complicated.

One thing that meditating does is improve your sense of humor. My mother has developed a keen one and constantly says witty things. Last week one of my boyfriends and I went out with my parents to the movies. We sat in the back of the car cracking up. My mother was real funny.

Since I've been making a good case for TM, I might as well tell you one more story. I know it sounds far-fetched, but I swear it's true and I don't lie. Even before I started meditating I was known for being a stickler for the truth.

The girl involved lives near us and when she was fifteen she was sent to a mental institution because she had tried to commit suicide several times and did lots of other kooky things. She was involved with psychoanalysis for two years. When they let her out, the doctors said she had to be very careful because the slightest stress might set her off. Well, she heard about TM and tried it. After six months she has a new lease on life. Sounds like a phony story? Everything I said is true!

In fact, her psychiatrist was so amazed that he started meditating, and if it's good enough for him it certainly is good enough for me!

The Innovating Educator-Meditator

A superintendent of schools is usually regarded as a pretty stuffy person, but Dr. S.C.T. defies that description. He is head of a school system in a middle-income community in lower New York state. He is held in high esteem by other professional administrators because he has never been afraid to try new and dramatic academic programs and because he has made the learning experience rich and rewarding.

When Dr. S.C.T. discovered that transcendental meditation worked for his students he decided to try it himself. As a result, he is more soft-spoken but fortunately still as dynamic!

It should be apparent to everyone connected with public schools that we have neither the number of teachers necessary, nor adequate facilities or equipment, to meet the challenge of modern education. There are few communities wealthy enough to provide that kind of miracle-size stuff—certainly not our community.

Therefore, it became quite evident that we had to go outside our school seeking assistance. In our particular case, we used a very simple administrative technique. We sent letters out to each adult in the district asking if they would help us, by utilizing either their vocational skills or their avocational interests, for enhancing or promoting our instructional programs. Amazing kinds of responses were received. One of them was a telephone call from a trained meditator who lived in the community. She claimed that students in TM programs made better grades.

Skepticism is too mild a word to describe my feelings, but I felt that if there was one grain of truth —that if TM could help the kids—I should learn more about it. I asked the woman to come and visit. She did, and during our conversation a number of points sounded most interesting.

I have always regarded myself as a very practical, day-to-day "nuts and bolts" administrator, but after consulting with some of my principals and vice-principals I decided to go ahead. We set aside a double-sized classroom for the TM lecture and discovered there was such an overflow of students and parents curious about meditation that we had to open a whole school building.

During the next few months dozens of youngsters in our junior and senior high school started meditating. Evidence appears to support the following:

1. Students improve their grades.
2. Students get along better with teachers.
3. Students get along better with parents.
4. Students get along better with other students.
5. Use of drugs lessens.

Earlier this week I met a young man who had formerly been a severe disciplinary problem. We had tried many things but nothing worked. Then he started meditating. I was told the results were good, but still I was surprised when we talked. His eyes had softened. He no longer jumped a half mile when he shook hands. His mouth formed a happy smile. All his mannerisms had taken a turn for the better. Just looking at him it was obvious TM had worked for him.

The Happy Housewife-Secretary Who Likes TM and Women's Lib

"I'm now very happy and comfortable in the life I lead," says Mrs. M.J., "and I credit it all to transcendental meditation." Whatever the reason, she does indeed appear to lead a contented life. She and her family live near Philadelphia, where she works as a

private secretary and defines her role as, "full-time-part-time wife, mother, employee, housekeeper." She is a great exponent of Women's Lib and feels that it is very compatible with TM. "After all," she adds, "they both have the same objective—happier people."

I remember sitting under a hair drier reading about how the Beatles and Mia Farrow practice something called transcendental meditation. I kept thinking it was all part of a publicity stunt or that it indicated how gullible show biz people really were. Couldn't they see that this meditating business was just a pack of nonsense?

Three years later other people thought I was just as gullible when I started meditating. I have nothing to do with show business—I'm a secretary in a business far removed from the entertainment field. I'm also a wife and mother.

One day about two years ago my nineteen-year-old son came home from college and said, "Ma, I got something for us to do." He was so excited that I didn't ask questions and went along with him to a transcendental meditation center. The next thing I knew I was meditating.

My biggest hang-up at first was that I regarded TM as just another form of religion. I'm not religious, yet I wasn't very happy to undertake another way of worshiping God. This hung me up for awhile, but the more I meditated, the more I realized that TM had nothing at all to do with religion. I started relaxing, and that was when the results happened. Even Mr. "Believe It or Not" Ripley would regard some of the results as stranger than fiction.

For years I had a nervous tic in my eye. It was

really bad when I was tired, but it also appeared when I wasn't tired. My friends tried not to mention it, but I knew they were constantly aware of it. Well, you know what? Within a few weeks of meditating the tic was gone. And it has stayed away.

I also had a history of colitis. As a rule, I steered clear of eating spicy foods and out of necessity I watched my diet carefully. Now I find I'm no longer in that situation and can handle all kinds of food, even very spicy curries.

I'd use the colitis as an excuse for being late to the office. I disliked everything about my job. I used to describe my boss as a real schizoid and would get uptight the moment I entered his office. I carried that feeling home and took it out on my husband and the kids. I'd feel guilty that I was deserting them for the office and that I wasn't attending enough PTA meetings. Things like that. It marred me physically and whatever I ate would be tied in knots.

I think it's all changed. Take yesterday, for example. It was Thursday and I got out of bed at 7:30. My husband handed me some orange juice, I took my shower, and meditated for twenty minutes. Then we had some oatmeal, toast, and coffee. When we finished eating we went off to work and I got to the office five minutes early.

It was a pleasant day. I had a great deal to do, but I didn't feel I was under great pressure, and I could complete the work. I didn't feel that if somehow I didn't finish everything the world would come to an end. I had lunch with the girls in the office. We went to a new Italian restaurant and I suggested what we'd have.

The kids were coming home from school that night and I was looking forward to seeing them. The family spent the entire evening together without fighting once! Believe me, that was very different from the past.

My daughter told an amusing but significant story about meditation. She was out driving with her boyfriend and she announced that she was going to meditate. He doesn't. She closed her eyes and when she finished she said it had been a very pleasant meditation. He said, "Wow, you know, as soon as you shut your eyes, I lost myself. I suddenly didn't know where I was and drove aimlessly up one street and down another. It was as if you had meditated and I had transcended!"

It was an entertaining story and maybe not so outlandish. My husband doesn't meditate, but I can see changes in him since I've started TM. Through the years when you live with somebody, you have these neurotic interplays. You know how to trigger each other off. It can be very destructive and very devastating. We used to play this game. But it hasn't happened in a long, long time. I stopped feeling hostile and no longer had the desire to quarrel. At first he'd start egging me on, but when he saw I wouldn't respond he stopped. I don't have the exact explanation, but I feel *my* meditating has helped *him*. He's seen what TM has done, and I firmly believe he wants to start, but maybe is afraid of the unknown. Eventually he'll come around. After all, in TM there is nothing to be afraid of and as FDR used to say, "There's nothing to fear but fear itself."

If I had started meditating earlier, I believe I'd have been a better wife and mother. I'd have been a great deal more relaxed and would have been emotionally better off. My children meditate and I can see definite results. There used to be great sibling rivalry.

You can't imagine how they despised one another! It was really horrible, really terrible. Now I actually think they like each other. I have this marvelous feeling about my children—that they're going to be great. I credit TM with the change.

Before I started meditating, I'd get depressed and break into tears about everything. A hungry kid someplace would set me off, or the conditions in prisons, or even my next door neighbor's dress shrinking. I'm still compassionate, but I no longer feel I have to be depressed to show concern.

Last year I met the Maharishi at a lecture I attended at the University of Massachusetts. I thought he was such a cute little man. He's tiny, so tiny. And then he opened his mouth and I was overwhelmed by his presence. He is an educated man and has a degree in physics. He said many things, but I was particularly impressed by one of his comments: "TM is a technique that is as ancient as mankind and universal in application. There are times in history that we can learn much from our fathers." I thought him quite articulate, but felt that he should have added, "and mothers."

A Drug User Kicks the Habit

The institution that treated T.L.J. filed his case under, "complicated drug anomie." Although he is only in his mid-twenties he looks much older. His lengthy period with drugs has taken its toll.

T.L.J. started taking "hard stuff" near the beginning of his unhappy career. He says honestly, "Even though I was mostly connected with acid I tried every conceivable drug known. I'm a true and blue veteran of the drug war."

He is typical of many young people we spoke to. Although critics say the definitive scientific test on the value of TM, as applied to drug users, has not been conducted, his case history is further evidence that transcendental meditation may prove to be the "miracle nondrug."

I am 25 years old and that, in itself, is something of a surprise. There have been moments when I doubted I'd ever make it—or even wanted to, in fact. My name isn't important. So many others—friends, acquaintances, others I never knew—have lived through strikingly similar experiences. For me, it began when I was thirteen years old, when I took my first long, deep swallow of cough medicine.

I was born in Brooklyn, but we moved out to Long Island after my mother, who was separated from my father when I was five, remarried. At least once a month I come back into Brooklyn to see my old friends. One weekend they were all just sitting around and drinking cough medicine. I mean, they were really getting into it. I didn't relate cough medicine to drugs at all. They said they were getting high, so I thought the feeling would be the same as drinking liquor. Hell, I thought, if you could get high drinking a little bottle of cough medicine rather than a couple of quarts of beer, this was for me.

The first time I tried it I got high, but the experience itself was so new I didn't recognize it as a drug high. The next night, having nothing else to do, we did it again. This time I felt it. I started getting these sensations throughout my whole body, and I really dug it. I came back into Brooklyn the next weekend, and the weekend after that; every weekend, in fact. I even started doing it at home, more and more often.

After awhile, the effect I was getting wasn't quite what it had been. I wasn't getting as high, so I had to up the amount. It got ridiculous. So, to help me get up, I started taking goofballs and smoking grass while I was drinking the syrup. I celebrated my fourteenth birthday flying.

Pot wasn't a big problem. At that point it just wasn't what it is today. In fact, I was the only one in my whole school who did smoke, and because of that I gained a reputation of being the school drug addict. I guess I really was. Every weekend I'd go into Brooklyn and we'd turn new people on or just sit around taking pot, pills, and syrup together. We were together, or so we thought.

This went on for about a year and, just as it'd happened before, I needed more and more to get high. So I started using stronger stuff. I wasn't smoking very much—just enough to enhance whatever else I was taking. The basic high was the narcotic, the drug that suppressed the nervous system. Finally, we went up the whole shopping list and reached heroin. It wasn't much of a jump from cough syrup. I'm convinced that cough syrup—the codeine—is worse for you than heroin. When you're into that stuff, the point at which you get high is always close to the point of an overdose. Heroin gets you right up there. Besides, heroin was more economical. It was costing me more to buy enough goofballs to get high than it did to buy heroin. The first time I shot it I was fifteen years old and felt a really nice rush. I really liked it. I was really into it.

I never managed to comprehend that these drugs might be damaging my body. I'm sure I knew it, but I just couldn't relate to it. I was taking them to get high and they were getting me high. End of fear.

It got to the point where I was getting high every

day. I can't estimate how expensive my habit was because I used a lot of things I got from drugstores. You have no idea how easy it is to forge a prescription, and because I could usually get what I needed from my friendly pharmacist I rarely relied on street heroin. I continued getting high as often as possible for three years, dropping out of high school on the way.

When I was eighteen, I threw down whatever I could get my hands on, anything that would get me high, get me up. I'd be terrible if I couldn't get any drugs. You couldn't talk to me, or expect a rational response from me. Drugs were my only enjoyment. I started turning other people on . . . to everything . . . unfortunately.

I was so . . . I guess hypersensitive is the word. I'd start crying in the middle of a sentence, often for no reason at all. I couldn't deal with anything. I couldn't handle any responsibility at all. I considered myself a parasite. Although I was still basically living at home, I began to spend more and more time on the streets. I never really got into stealing, though I did take money from my parents. They knew what I was into, and they tried to stop me, but of course they couldn't do it.

Finally, I reached the point where I really wanted to go to a hospital. Because I was only eighteen, my mother had to sign me in, but every time I was supposed to meet her, something would happen. Maybe I'd fall out somewhere, and I'd miss her. She screamed that I really didn't want help. I really didn't, not in the same sense she meant. I did want to get into that damn hospital, though. One day I decided I'd go home, stay overnight, and we'd go check me in in the morning. I almost made it. I went home with a few goofballs in my pocket and took them. I really got stoned and had a huge argument with my mother and stepfather. They threw me out of the house. In a fit of anger, I heaved a rock through the front window.

I thought better of it the next morning and decided to go home. While I was sitting there, trying to talk to my mother, trying to make some sense out of something I didn't understand, my stepfather called the police. They arrested me for malicious mischief.

Jail was funny—it was the best of times and it was the worst of times. It was the low point of my life. I was in jail with no one willing to put up bail money. I had no friends at all. I was rejected by everyone. I must have looked like a complete mess—sloppy, very pale—and I can understand why no one wanted to be around me. But in jail I first began to realize what I was doing to myself. I first began to see there was something greater than the things I'd known, though I really didn't know what it was.

Jail was rough. Drug withdrawal is a very dangerous thing. The doses should be cut down gradually, but I was completely cut off. I had terrible convulsions. I was terribly depressed. At that moment, if I'd had a choice, I might have chosen to stop the world right there. But I was lucky, I kicked. The judge decided to give me what they called an "Article Nine"—I'd go free, with a suspension of course, if I would agree to stay in an institution for at least three months. After looking around, my mother suggested one, a center for former drug addicts. I really didn't want to go, but I had no choice. I knew I needed something, so I went.

I stayed eighteen months, all totally drug free. I didn't touch anything for over two and a half years. When I was twenty-one, I left the institution for good and began working for Nassau County in the local drug rehabilitation program. But I was having trouble on the outside. I couldn't relate to straight people. And I was disgusted with people who were into junk —once I had pulled myself out of that gutter. That left practically nobody.

The institution's philosophy was based on the premise that you'd never, ever, use any type of drugs again. But if you thought you could handle alcohol, you were allowed to drink. I kind of resented that because I thought alcohol was a lot worse than pot. We'd been told that if we smoked grass we'd be back on the hard stuff before we knew it. I thought that was a lot of crap.

One night, another institution graduate and I decided to experiment. We'd go to Greenwich Village and, if we happened to run into a party where they were smoking, we'd smoke. We didn't have to wait very long. As soon as we parked our car, two guys came up and asked if we'd like to buy an ounce. So we freaked. We smoked. Got high. I was still working at the center, but that didn't last very long. I just couldn't remain in that scene once I got into psyche-delics. I began experimenting with ups and downs and, a couple of weeks after that trip into the Village, I got into LSD. My first trip was good, nothing fantastic, but nice and comfortable. I saw hundreds of colors—designs of all shapes—flowing by. I moved my hands, and they were followed by gold lines and more colors. I knew LSD was for me.

I didn't feel there was any contradiction between the philosophy I'd been given and psychedelic drugs. We'd been taught to grow up, to expand our horizons, to expand our awareness of ourselves—and these drugs were helping me do exactly that. I thought I was coming in contact with myself, which I saw as a very positive thing. I had myself convinced that I was using these drugs to become an adult. And I knew these drugs had no connection with the old junk I'd been taking: then I was turning myself off; now I was turning on, expanding my perception.

My first four LSD trips were calm and cool. The fifth was a bad one. I was at a party with all straight people, and I felt like there were thousands of voices aimed at me—just pouring into me. There was nothing I could do about it, they wouldn't stop. Before long I smoked every day. I was always high. I was using mescaline, pot, hash, acid, and, occasionally, speed. This went on for two years.

There were a few bright spots in those years. At a party one night I met a girl who was just as deeply into psychedelics as I was. She was on downs that night, and I thought she was really cool. I didn't see her for six months after that, but one night we met again at a friend's house. That night we dropped some acid and sort of fell into each other. Three months later we were married.

She was high for the ceremony, and after the wedding we continued using drugs. We met a lot of addicts, got high a lot, turned a lot of people on. It was really an ego trip to turn people on. We were even doing some dealing on a reasonably regular basis, more to turn other people on than to make money.

We began losing weight. We couldn't sleep. Our skin broke out in hives. I'm putting it mildly when I say that life was a living death. One day, we saw the Maharishi's picture in the newspaper, and out of desperation my wife and I went to the transcendental meditation lecture. Someone had told us that the Maharishi could help, but he wasn't there. We were disappointed but suddenly discovered Jerry Jarvis.* He was really together, and I was fascinated by the way he related TM to physiology.

We went back for the second lecture and decided to be initiated. We felt this was something that might be for us when Jarvis explained TM consisted of an effortless technique, and was something to be lived. He also neglected to mention any spiritualism. Rather, he spoke of something that was already inside everyone and just had to be brought out.

Neither of us really liked it when we were told we had to stay off all drugs for fifteen days before being initiated. Our friends continued to smoke and thought we were a little weird for stopping so suddenly. It took some will power on both our parts to stay off. This was the first time in a long time that I exhibited any signs of will power. I remember thinking, "Maybe this will work."

The moment I was initiated I knew it would. Almost from that moment, my wife and I gave up drugs. It was not something we talked about, or decided. It just happened. We hadn't intended to. I'm not even sure we wanted to, but we did.

Two weeks after we had started meditating, we did smoke, but we found there was absolutely no reason to. We had found what we were looking for. With TM I've tasted that same experience—that same wonderful inner understanding—that I had on LSD a few times. It's not exactly the same, but it's close enough for me to know I'll eventually reach the state of fulfillment I'm looking for.

Where am I now? I'm happy and increasingly

---

* Jerry Jarvis, one of the first American meditators and currently national director of SIMS and also the International Meditation Society.

getting happier. I know now what it is I'm looking for. I have a steady job as a construction worker and get good pay. I get along with my parents now and, although I've made a point of trying not to turn people on to TM, several are considering trying it, simply because of the change it caused in me. My wife is more fulfilled than I am, if that's possible. We've decided to become teachers of TM. *You get so thankful that you want to instruct others.* I know I'll never go back to psychedelics, or any drugs at all.

Not everyone that I know who's been on drugs has tried TM successfully. Some have, a few haven't. But in each case the ones who failed are those who gave up after a few weeks—without even giving their systems a chance to purge themselves of the effects of the drugs. Is TM a cure for drugs? As far as I'm concerned, it certainly is.

The Pragmatic Engineer

Dr. B.D.H., in his early forties, is regarded as one of the country's leading industrial engineers. The government frequently seeks him out for advice. His colleagues refer to him as "The main spoke in the main wheel." In addition to being a top-level consultant to several important firms, he teaches engineering at a large Eastern university.

By profession I'm an engineer and engineers are usually very pragmatic fellows. We have to be, since we constantly deal with many different kinds of people—from conservative hardhats to illusionary artists who rarely come down to earth. Out of necessity, I've learned to evaluate all sorts of abstract ideas.

My education has been quite materialistic, and transcendental meditation was completely out of my normal interests. It was by haphazard chance that I started meditating. I was out for a short walk near my home and noticed a poster advertising a lecture on TM. It sounded so unusual to me as an engineer that I decided to go in. I was prepared for a great deal of fuzzy, in-the-clouds gibberish, but the lecture was given by a very clear-minded young man who didn't approach it from the mystical side at all. He spoke in very pragmatic terms. His main point seemed to be that TM was a way of increasing your mental awareness and that through meditation you had more energy available to you.

He appeared to make sense, and I found what he said appealing. At that time I was under a great deal of pressure, so I figured I had little to lose by trying transcendental meditation. And so I did. But I must admit that the initiation procedure put me off. The idea of bringing a handkerchief, flowers, and sweet fruit seemed like a dichotomy of purpose. In retrospect, I now find it a beautiful ceremony—but still irrelevant to meditating. However, a friend of mine who is also an engineer and who is just as hard-nosed as I am, feels the initiation ceremony is extremely meaningful.

He believes that he has had outstanding results with TM. He was going through a very rough time in his profession and with his family—everything was wrong. He had turned to alcohol for solace. Then he started meditating, and all of a sudden things began to look great. From an obscure—if you wish—engineer, he has become one of the outstanding men in his field. His relations with his family improved vastly, and he cut out drinking rather spontaneously. I'd say things have definitely worked out well. I hesitate to credit it all to TM, but I suspect that it is substantially because of it.

The TM results in my case aren't so spectacular, but I seem now to be more at ease with other people and have a better grasp of what they're trying to ask me. There appears to be a greater degree of communication. I've become very tranquil about new situations.

My sleep pattern has changed somewhat. Before, I occasionally had trouble falling asleep, but now, the moment I hit the pillow I drift off. I may sleep slightly less than I used to, but then I don't feel that I require as much sleep, and I always feel rested. Another dividend that's accrued is that I used to think there was something very virtuous about rising when it was still dark outside. Well, now I still feel guilty about an extra hour of sleep—but less guilty. I seem to be living a broader time span than I did formerly and am more cognizant of time.

I must admit that some people feel there are some negative results from TM. In some instances, meditating brings on brief periods of dizziness and disorientation. It has happened to me. They last for two or three minutes and gradually diminish and vanish. Scientists have told me that's the crux of the whole thing—that you are transcending at these periods and that when you come back from transcending, you release enormous amounts of stress in a short period. This, of course, upsets your physiological metabolism. But since you have transcended, you have so much energy that you are able to overcome this rather quickly.

Another thing I encountered during and after meditation was a buzzing sound in my ears. As a matter of fact, I have it right now. It's like background static and varies in tonality. When you start meditating, it surrounds you like a big blanket. When you're not meditating, it recedes into a very small point. I guess it's with me all the time—only I'm now conscious of it. If I had to think of it, yes, I'd know that it was there. I can't construe it to be either good or bad. I just don't really think of it. Certainly it's offset by the tranquility experience when you come out of meditation.

TM, you're told, functions in a very rational way —bang, bang, bang, and so on; you do this, then you do that, and eventually you'll reach this state, which is very simple and very natural. But you're skeptical at the beginning, as I was. In fact, these steps do start to materialize in greater or smaller degrees, and then you say, "They told me that A was going to happen and A happened. And B was going to happen and truly it happened. Maybe it might follow that C, D, E, and eventually Z will also come into being."

Well, I accept it. It gives you a great depth and a greater promise of religion. You have to swallow a whole thing in gospel truth and really hit the moment of reality the moment you die.

I tend to believe that if I were not an engineer, if I were a medical doctor or a lawyer, I'd be a little more unhesitant in my praising meditation. I think there is a great deal to be praised. It's just my training and my profession that will not let me make unconditional claims. I plan to continue to meditate, for the very reason that there are indications that it is good. I'd unquestionably advise others to meditate.

The Army's TM Advocate

Major General Franklin M. Davis is a most unusual meditator and an unusual Army officer. He first "discovered" transcendental meditation while working in the Pentagon, trying to find a solution to the military's drug problem. Besides having served through three wars, he is an accomplished author. He has written a dozen soft-cover suspense and adventure novels, one very well received hard-cover book detailing the occupation of Germany (Come as Conquerers) and more than one hundred short stories and articles for national magazines. In 1971 he became Commandant of the U.S. Army War College, in Carlisle, Pa., as well as Commanding General of the U.S. Army Military History Research Collection.

I'm a career soldier. I've seen a great part of this world, served in three wars, saw combat in two, was wounded in one, and lost a son in the same war. I joined the Army as a second lieutenant in 1940, having graduated from the Massachusetts State College (now the University of Massachusetts) with an ROTC commission—and no job offers. Although at that time ROTC graduates didn't have to serve in the regular army, the hundred and forty-three dollars monthly lieutenant's pay looked mighty good and, as my father said, "You didn't have to be a genius to see there was a war coming." Joining the army was a decision I've never regretted.

My last tour of duty outside this country was in Vietnam. I was the Commander of the 199th Light Brigade, operating south of Saigon. We were on river assault craft coming up a canal when the Viet Cong took our boats under fire. I received twenty steel fragments in my face and had both ears blown in. And that, indirectly, is how I came to be interested in transcendental meditation.

I was sent stateside for an ear operation, but an

infection had set in and they couldn't operate until it cleared up, so I was temporarily assigned to the Pentagon, to the office of the deputy chief of staff for personnel. My job was director of personnel studies and research, and therefore I spent quite a bit of time with behavioral scientists. Also, because our office was not in the Pentagon itself, but in a nearby building we shared with a moving company and which had no cafeteria, I used to eat lunch outside the building. This gave me time to renew a lot of old acquaintances I'd made the last time I was stationed in Washington. One was a lady who is working her way up the ranks in the Department of Health, Education and Welfare. She is a bright, energetic woman whose opinion I have a great deal of respect for. She was the first person to tell me about transcendental meditation.

After six months in the personnel office I was made director of military personnel policies. That meant I was responsible for finding solutions to a myriad of problems hitting the military: racial tension, discipline, law and order, promotions, awards and medals, enlistment standards, officer-selection standards, and drug abuse. In short, I was the guy in charge of disasters.

I hadn't been in the job very long when I realized what the real disaster was going to be—the army had a major drug abuse problem on its hands, even though it wouldn't surface publicly for another six months. Talking to men coming back from Vietnam, it was obvious that eventually this was going to bust wide open.

Not that the Defense Department hadn't been aware of the magnitude of the problem. Numerous studies had been done, and there was some effort to get a more enlightened drug policy passed. At this point (spring 1969) drug abuse was still considered a criminal offense, not at all a social or medical problem. The policy was simple: "There's only one answer for the drug user—jail."

It was obvious we were going about it in the wrong way because the problem was increasing. Like society in general, we were so busy looking for rehabilitation methods we'd never given much thought to prevention. The army had no really good preventive movement. There was too much accent on identification, curing, and rehabilitation. We had nothing to give the soldier except some army field manuals and a comic book with some supposedly scary pictures in it. So I started working on prevention. The people who knew the most about it, I found out at lunch one day, were my old friends at HEW, who were helping to produce materials on the drug problem for the government. My friend and her son talked to me at length about something called transcendental meditation and explained that there seemed to be a very high potential for drug-abuse prevention in the movement.

I thought: now just what is transcendental meditation? The name turned me off at first. It sounded too kinky, too spooky. Although I hate to admit it, being in this uniform and this business, I guess I was pretty establishment oriented. I was also aware that as an army general officer you have to be careful what causes you espouse or someone's going to send for the net. The major thing that kept me from being totally skeptical, and perhaps forgetting the whole thing, was the fact that I'd spent a year in Cambodia in the late 1950s. During that time I did a lot of traveling and gained a great deal of respect for Eastern philosophies. Maybe TM, or the Maharishi Mahesh Yogi, wasn't quite as nutty as I might have otherwise thought, but it did smack a little of voodooism just the same.

On the other hand, I said to myself, I ought to be at least enlightened enough to give new ideas a chance, and the more I explored, the more fascinated I became. I discovered that youngster after youngster had given up drugs when they started meditating. I learned there were some people of excellent scientific repute, like Drs. Benson and Wallace at Harvard, doing top-flight work on the subject. I saw there was a great deal of what our people would call anecdotal evidence, meaning just bits and pieces, but there was also some strong scientific basis for the fact that youngsters who got into TM would move away from drugs.

The way I described it at the time was that they were turning on with their minds rather than drugs, although I knew that TM was not a substitute for drugs. In the end, though, three things really made me decide to investigate: the confidence that the people at HEW had in TM; a lecture I attended at Georgetown University during a particularly hectic week on campus that a couple of hundred kids found time to attend; and, finally, the truly amazing results of the Wallace-Benson drug survey.

So, quietly, I began seriously exploring transcendental meditation in terms of the needs of the military. I talked to youngsters. I talked to people at the Students International Meditation Society (SIMS) in Washington. I spoke with scientists at the Stanford Research Institute and discovered physiological evidence that I didn't know about; some meditators had lower vital signs, heart rate, blood pressure, and even pulse rate than when they were asleep—thus TM had potential space travel value. The more I checked, the more interested I got.

I went to the army chaplain and made sure there were no religious objections. There weren't. I went to the army medical people and, although they kept saying, "Well, this isn't very scientific," they did nothing to discourage me. No one did, as a matter of fact.

Finally I realized the time had come to do something about my research. I knew if I put out orders saying, "Everyone file out for meditation," I'd be too arbitrary, and it wouldn't work with troops. TM has to come from an individual. He has to want to start. So what we did was start a lecture course at the service club at Ft. Myer, Va. We put up a few posters and had a respectable turnout. We kept this program going and we're really beginning to make progress. It was right around this time that the army drug-abuse problem hit the headlines. The reports from Vietnam began rolling in and the size of the problem became obvious. Since it is army policy to attempt to send a man back into society a better person than he was when he first came in, we set up an entire new staff agency to deal solely with this problem.

By this time (winter 1970) I felt that, in order for me even to try to sell this to the army, I'd have to take the course myself, on the theory that you shouldn't ask troops to do something you haven't tried or can't do. I realized there were possible consequences, that I was going to get into it personally now, and some people were going to think I was nuts. But it wasn't a hard decision to make. I said: obviously I believe in it, and if I'm trying to get the institution committed to it, I figured I'd better know everything about it. So I said what the hell, and went ahead. In February 1971 I became a meditator.

I was initiated at the SIMS center in Washington. I must have seemed a bit strange to most of the people there because I had to go there directly from my office and therefore had my uniform on. Next to a little, gray-haired woman, at fifty-three I was the oldest one there. And a soldier, a general, to boot!

I did my best to make everyone feel comfortable. I'd walk in the door, and as they all turned around I'd say something silly like, "Okay, you're all drafted." My initiation was no different than anyone else's. I brought a white handkerchief, flowers, and two plums and a pear. And then I began meditating.

It took two weeks before I got any results. I hadn't really expected any, or been looking for any, but there they were! My blood pressure went down 10 points; my wife said my disposition improved a great deal (although I thought it was fine before); and I found that the minor stresses and strains of life around Washington didn't bother me anymore. I suddenly discovered I had stopped griping at other drivers, for example.

I think everyone will admit that my occupation makes me a little unusual in the movement, and so I really wasn't surprised when the SIMS people asked me to speak at their summer symposium (1971) on creative intelligence, at the University of Massachusetts. It was there that I met the Maharishi for the first time. I was taken to his door, asked to remove my shoes and escorted into his hotel room. He was sitting on his mat, on a bed, his legs carefully crossed.

He shook my hand and said, "How do you do, it's so nice what you have done for us."

This sort of startled me. I didn't feel I had done anything. Then he smiled and said, "you know, we've given this the wrong name, it turns people off." I think he'd like to change the name to "creative intelligence," and I think he'd be right. Recently a reporter said to me, "The name transcendental meditation scares off a lot of people, especially the Establishment types." He's right, too, and I think that that's too bad, because they're the people who can really gain from TM.

At the seminar, which was attended by Buckminster Fuller, among others, I spoke briefly on TM and the army. Many people ask me how I can reconcile the army, which is an instrument for war, and TM, which is an instrument for peace. It's quite easy. No one hates war more than a true soldier because we know how bad it is.

Basically, I'm as big a peacenik as you'll find. I've always thought a good solution to the problem would be to take some of the zealots who help start these things and have them walk through a ward of wounded. And I firmly believe TM can help soldiers think before they act, and act on that thought. The army is also an instrument of peace. If given the chance and proper training, assuredly, our soldiers can benefit from TM.

The first publicity I received came from the seminar. Photographers took a photograph of me in full uniform standing next to the Maharishi in full sheet. The photo was printed as far away as Australia, and I'm sure some of the people outside the army must have looked at me a little askance, and said, "What kind of nut is this, running around with gurus?"

I don't apologize for a single thing. I wouldn't change a word or a thing I did because I feel quite strongly that TM has a good chance of helping us with some very tough problems.

The army still hasn't committed itself, but it is softening up. Certainly my superior officers have been sympathetic right down the line. We're starting at a very low key, but our growth has been encouraging. Recently, for example, the First Army had a drug workshop and asked me to speak about TM.

Right now, we've got programs running at Ft. Knox, Ft. Dix, Ft. Myer, Ft. Belvoir, and other places, all on an unofficial, low-key basis. I am totally convinced that TM is a possible means of curbing the military drug problem. In my research I've found that many youngsters turn to drugs because of their inability to adjust to a totally new, totally different situation. This system offers a reasonable approach for a youngster to make the very difficult necessary adjustment between himself and his new surroundings, from within. Personal stability has a great deal to do with keeping off drugs, and I think this is what TM can offer—this great stability.

I certainly don't think that TM is too far-fetched for the army. We've changed. We've had to. The Vietnam experience has changed us, the push for a modern army has changed us; the fact that we've had to meet the draftee toe-to-toe, head-to-head, and explain our case, has changed us. We've had to take a hard look at ourselves and decide what it was that was good, and what was bad. We knew we had lost communication when we saw kids burning draft cards. All this has opened our eyes to things that are happening around us, things that years ago would have been laughed at in army circles. TM is one of those things.

The program I'd like to see, recognizing the fact that an individual has to decide on his own to try meditation, would be one that offers the maximum opportunity for a soldier to meditate, or learn TM, at no cost to himself. And it would be made available during selected time periods, not when he would be forced to make a hard decision between going downtown or sitting through lectures. And I think TM should be under the banner of those most concerned with human relations, our education people. I know we can't force anyone to meditate. The minute we say, "Okay soldier, get over there and get your TM!" we've lost them.

I have great hopes for TM and the army. It is a relationship that we can certainly benefit by. I know, because I have.

6

Everything You Need to Know About TM

"*At first most people are skeptical. Few believe in miracles, even small ones that transcendental meditation produces,*" says an official of SIMS. "*And when an individual is first introduced to TM, many questions run through his mind. They are often the same, ranging from, 'Will it improve my sex life?' to 'How much is it going to cost me?'—and everything in between.*"

We gathered the questions most frequently asked and secured answers from physiologists, physicists, educators, psychiatrists, psychologists, meditators—and even from scoffers.

Why should I meditate?

To be happier and healthier. Study after study has shown that people who meditate are better adjusted and healthier than they were before they started meditating. Also, TM has, in many cases, eliminated the desire for drugs, cigarettes, and alcohol.

No one, of course, needs a daily dose of TM to survive, but those who do meditate claim it makes their daily life much better. The *Hospital Times of London* recently summed up the extensive research of Dr. Demetri P. Kanellakos: "TM increased energy and efficiency in performing any kind of work, increased tranquility of mind coupled with decreased physical and mental tension; partial or complete loss of desire for hallucinogenic and similar drugs, including alcohol; increased creativity, productivity, intuitiveness and so on; improvement in functional disorders such as poor body posture and insomnia; and better mobilization of body resources to meet adverse circumstances such as accidents, sensory monotony, and surgery."

Swimmers who meditate claim it helps them swim better, factory workers say they work better, engineers insist that meditation makes them more creative, students maintain they get better grades, mothers and fathers feel they become better parents. In every occupation, every walk of life, people who meditate contend it improves lives, and there is hard physical evidence to back them up. Experiments have proven that TM does indeed reduce the normal metabolic rate, decreases oxygen consumption, provides more "deep rest" than a full night's sleep and appears to have many other definite advantages.

"Before I began meditating I was awful," a twenty-seven-year-old graduate student remembered. "I was looking for happiness via chemicals, churches, and so on. One day a friend began TM. After I saw the change in him I became a meditator. I have noticed a total change in perceptual awareness. I've begun to clear the cobwebs, cut the static, and I see so clearly what is going on. My life style has changed from that of a selfish, scared violent little fellow to the life style of a benevolent, self-secure, nonviolent little fellow. I no longer fear the future or the past."

Can anyone be taught to meditate?

With a few specific exceptions, almost everyone can be taught to meditate. Those exceptions include individuals who are physiologically incapable of following the simplest instructions and, obviously, those who do not have sufficient command of the language the course is being taught in. Also, those people who are looked upon for advice by others—clergymen, social workers, psychiatrists—are asked to write a letter to the Maharishi explaining their reasons for wanting to be initiated. (This has come about since a Midwestern religious leader was discovered teaching TM after having been initiated himself, but not having taken any teaching courses.) Otherwise, as *Life Magazine* reported, "A prospective convert needs no preparation, no intellectual background and TM requires no repudiation of the past and no promise to behave in the future."

"The only generalization I can make," a SIMS administrator said, "is that most people that come here feel their life is not what it could be. That, in some direction, whether in terms of personal development, better health, getting along with other people, religious growth, they feel there could be something else. Something to give them more knowledge, more understanding. As to the type of people that start, it's pretty evenly broken down between men and women. We have been getting more people from colleges and the professional ranks than from the ghettos and trades. If I said that I really hear it from our construction workers and low-income meditators I wouldn't be telling it accurately."

Even so, isn't TM still mostly for young white hippies?

Wrong again. TM appeals to people of all races, creeds, color, and age. A four-year-old girl and an eighty-three-year-old great-grandmother recently became meditators. Almost every age and ethnic group is represented.

The movement is led by three groups: the Spiritual Regeneration Movement, which seems to attract many more older people than younger; Students International Meditation Society (SIMS) or just International Meditation Society, which centers mainly around young people; and TM Center, Inc., which is primarily oriented toward Blacks and the specific needs of the Black community. TM Center, Inc., is the newest offshoot and it is aimed at increasing the number of Black meditators in the country. Presently there are about twenty-five Black TM teachers in the country and there is a TM center in the Watts district of Los Angeles.

Although there is no age barrier, there is a special TM program for young people under the age of twelve. This technique, called "walking meditation," involves a mantra but does not involve sitting quietly with eyes closed. It is a simpler technique based on method rather than comprehension.

Meditation is spreading rapidly. The army has shown a great deal of interest in TM, in particular as a drug deterrent. And in an experiment recently conducted in a Western prison, five inmates were introduced to TM. All five were selected for their particularly antisocial behavior inside prison. All five have become model prisoners; two have been released on parole, and the other three are awaiting parole hearings.

You said almost anyone can meditate. How about the guy who takes drugs?

Even the guy who takes drugs. There is only one stipulation: Since drugs seem to have an effect on an individual's ability to learn the technique properly, the single requirement of an initiate is that he stop using nonprescription drugs for fifteen days before being initiated. Jerry Jarvis, national coordinator of SIMS, explained, "In this technique, the entire nervous system is used, and narcotics have a very strong effect on the nervous system. Some say it's good; some say it's bad; some say it's good and bad; but we believe in safety first, and we have found that those who have been free of all these drugs start very well." Once an individual has been initiated, there is nothing to prevent him from continuing to use drugs. However, there is strong evidence that TM replaces the need for drugs.

Are you saying transcendental meditation is a cure for drug abuse?

Possibly the most exciting use of TM involves drug abuse. To paraphrase a television commercial, "In case after case, transcendental meditation has been found to be an effective substitute for drugs when used regularly." In other words, there has been much evidence that there is a definite relationship between TM and drug abuse. Based on this evidence, there can be little doubt that, in many cases, TM does cure drug addiction.

Among the first to suggest publicly the connection between drug abuse and TM were the Beatles. "One thing that has happened to us because of the Maharishi," Paul McCartney said, "is that now we are off drugs. We have replaced them with transcendental meditation. The taking of drugs expands the consciousness; it is like taking an aspirin without having a headache."

Ringo Starr added, "You only take drugs when you are searching for something else. At the moment I have found what I am searching for by meditation." Reports started appearing that the Beatles' experience had not been isolated, that many drug users were finding an outlet in TM. Finally science decided to take a look at this unusual relationship.

In 1969 W. Thomas Winquist did a research paper for the U.C.L.A. department of sociology entitled, "The Effect of the Regular Practice of Transcendental Meditation on Students Involved in the Regular Use of Hallucinogenic and *Hard* Drugs." Winquist interviewed four hundred eight-four meditators and found that one hundred forty-three had been regular drug users prior to beginning TM. All one hundred forty-three smoked marijuana when they started meditating; 84 percent stopped completely (no use for a minimum of three months); 15 percent decreased (50 percent, or less, of prior usage for three consecutive months); and 1 percent increased in their use of marijuana.

Of the one hundred forty-three, one hundred eleven were using hallucinogenic drugs other than marijuana. Of these, 86 percent stopped and 14 percent decreased. And of the one hundred forty-three subjects, forty-two were using hard drugs before TM; after beginning to meditate 86 percent stopped and 14 percent decreased.

Winquist also asked his subjects, "If your use of drugs has changed since starting to meditate, state why." Although 15 percent gave no reason, 49 percent said that life became more fulfilling ("Life after meditation finally became satisfying. I no longer need drugs." "Since beginning meditation I now have peace of mind that I am on the fastest and safest road of consciousness expansion and evolution."); 21 percent stated that the drug experience became less pleasurable ("Three recent experiences by way of experiment proved temporarily dulling and moody. The continuance of drugs would be absurd."); 8 percent stated that the desire for drugs disappeared ("I didn't try to stop—after awhile I just found myself not taking them anymore."); and 4 percent had other reasons.

The Winquist survey produced the first substantial evidence that the connection between TM and decrease of drug abuse existed. One of the next steps was taken by Dr. Herbert Benson, an Assistant Professor of Medicine at Harvard Medical School. Dr. Benson studied 1,862 subjects who had been practicing TM for at least three months. In hearings before the United States Congress (House Committee on Crime) he summarized his results: "Following the start of the practice of TM, there was a marked decrease in the number of drug abusers in all categories. As the practice of meditation increased, the subjects progressively decreased their drug abuse until after twenty-one months of meditation most subjects had completely stopped using drugs. For example, in the six-month period before starting meditation, about 80 percent of the subjects used marijuana, and of those about 28 percent were heavy users. After practicing meditation six months, 37 percent used marijuana and of those only 6.5 percent were heavy users. After twenty-one months . . . only 12 percent continued to use marijuana, and only one individual was a heavy user."

Dr. Benson's report also stated:

> Transcendental meditation is acceptable among youthful drug abusers. It is offered as a program for personal development and is not specifically intended to be a treatment for drug abuse; the alleviation of drug abuse is merely a side effect of the practice. Thus, it may not threaten those beliefs of the committed abuser who condones the use of drugs.
>
> Eighteen hundred sixty-two subjects formed the basis of this study. These subjects significantly decreased or stopped abusing drugs; decreased or stopped engaging in drug selling activity; and changed their attitudes in the direction of discouraging others from abusing drugs after starting transcendental meditation.
>
> Transcendental meditation should be investigated as an alternative to drugs by a controlled, prospective study.

Dr. Benson then outlined the study he suggests should be made.

Major General Franklin Davis, currently serving as commander of the United States Army War College in Carlisle, Pennsylvania, also feels that TM offers strong hope for the drug user (see page 100).

Chris Meriam, prevention manager of the Governor's Office for Drug Abuse for the State of Michigan recently said, "We consider the transcendental meditation program a necessary ingredient to every drug-abuse education effort seriously concerned with providing strong and useful alternative life styles for its participants."

TM officials have made no concerted effort to popularize the connection between drug abuse and TM. "We don't want to broadcast the movement in terms of drugs," an Eastern regional leader said, "because it may turn off a lot of people who aren't using drugs."

Is transcendental meditation a religion?

No. Everyone involved in the practice of TM emphasizes that, although TM does stem from Eastern religious tradition, it is not a religion and has absolutely no religious overtones. "I could start a religion," the Maharishi once commented, "but it would limit my course because so many million men are tied to their religion. So now I apply to people of all religions and I do not try to convert them."

TM does not require any belief, understanding, moral code, or even agreement with the ideas and philosophy. It is defined by its teachers as a technique and a method, "just like brushing your teeth."

When pushed on the subject, Maharishi contrasted meditation centers and houses of worship, noting, "We have made our academies the center of scientific experiments. The experiences of men and women are tested and verified. With the deepest respect for established religion, I believe that we are better equipped to convince skeptics because we verify our results with modern, scientific means."

There is also no connection with religion in a physical sense. There is little structure to a TM meeting; informality is stressed, rather than the rigidity of some church services. There are no rewards promised for meditating (beyond personal gain) or threats leveled for not meditating. The centers themselves are simple and functional, with most furniture resembling neo-Grand Rapids, rather than the rich beauty of houses of worship.

Does TM interfere with the regular practice of religion?

Not at all. In fact, many meditators say TM reinforced their wavering religious beliefs. The Reverend Royal J. Parent, writing in *The Church World,* Maine's official Catholic church weekly, said, "I must explain that TM as it spreads to the four corners of the world will not do away with the Church; it will enhance it; its members will radiate and be more of a reflection of heaven on earth. This will not be limited to monks and others who devote their lives to contemplation, it will be the possession of all those who practice TM."

Although many nonmeditators feel strongly that their belief in the church provides the fuller life TM promises, practitioners claim that TM actually brings them closer to their religion. During an interview with Reverend Parent, a Catholic mother of three children said that TM has put her in a position to enjoy the postconciliar Church, and to get more enjoyment out of her daily Mass. "The Mass is celebration," she said, "and it becomes a greater source of joy with each celebration."

Dale Warner, a member of the Michigan House of Representatives and the former chairman of the House Committee on Narcotics, said in recommending TM, "Transcendental meditation has also proven fruitful in my growth as a Christian. I am a member of a conservative, independent Baptist church and my appreciation for and my understanding of Christian religious teaching has broadened and deepened considerably and wholesomely since beginning meditation."

Can TM help me stop smoking and drinking?

The answer, again, is yes—a definite yes! Meditators seem to have the same reaction to cigarette smoking and alcohol consumption as they do toward drugs—once meditation starts, use of the others decreases. In the summary of his aforementioned study, Dr. Herbert Benson told the Congressional committee: "The subjects decreased their use of 'hard' alcoholic beverages and smoking. The magnitude of these changes increased with the length of time the subject practiced transcendental meditation."

Questionnaires were given by Dr. Benson and his staff to 1,950 subjects who had been practicing transcendental meditation for three months or more. The questionnaire was completed by 1,862 subjects.

Of that number, 503 considered themselves "heavy" cigarette smokers; 180 were medium smokers; 203 classified themselves light smokers. After twenty-two to thirty-three months only 49 people were still smoking heavily. Thirty-four of the "medium" group were still smoking and 55 people were still smoking "lightly."

The results were similar for those who used alcohol. Originally, 50 people considered themselves heavy drinkers. Within twenty-two to thirty-three months, that number was reduced to three. Two hundred ninety-five were "medium" drinkers, a number that fell to 22; "light" users, originally numbering 770, decreased to 187.

There is also much anecdotal evidence attesting to TM's role in smoking and drinking. Thousands of men and women insist that they stopped smoking and drinking after they started meditation.

When an individual begins meditating, there is usually no immediate sign that he will not drink or smoke anymore. Rather, as one Queens, N.Y. housewife put it, "When my husband and I began meditating, I smoked three packs of cigarettes a day. He came home from work and had at least three quick drinks. Now (two months later) I'm down to less than one pack. I haven't done it purposely. I've just kind of forgotten to pick up a cigarette, and my husband has cut out his before-dinner drinking."

A recent article on TM in the *Mensa Journal* (for people with superior IQ's) was reprinted by one of that organization's older members and sent out with this comment: "This article is sent to you by a Mensan in Alcoholics Anonymous who was induced by the article to try TM, and has found it useful for release from nervous tension and as an adjunct to the A.A. program."

There is no fifteen-day abstention period for either smokers or drinkers before being initiated. TM teachers feel that alcohol and tobacco don't have the same clouding effect on the nervous system that drugs do.

When is the best time to meditate?

Ideally, you should meditate directly before a period of activity because TM provides extra energy. For that reason it is recommended that meditation be broken up into two daily twenty-minute periods: the first in the morning; the second in the evening before dinner. The morning meditation should take place after you've given your body a few minutes to awaken fully; otherwise you may fall back to sleep. The evening meditation should be done early at night, because the deep rest obtained from meditating makes it possible for you to engage in physical or mental activities followed by a restful night's sleep.

Since it is the cumulative effects of TM that yield the most benefits, it is very important that an individual stick to his regularly scheduled meditation periods. Although an instant meditation in the midst of a busy day at the office or after a fight with your spouse might indeed make you feel better, in the long run it will hinder your progress. Meditation experts prefer that meditators not use it as an emotional Bandaid.

You also should definitely not meditate directly after eating. TM slows down the metabolic rate of your body and hence interferes with your digestive system. Therefore, meditation after eating may lead to discomfort and nausea.

If it's so good, why should I meditate for only twenty minutes?

After interviewing thousands of meditators, the Maharishi says, "Twenty minutes in the morning and twenty minutes in the evening is plenty." Given less, your system does not get the full benefits of TM. More than that defeats the purpose of TM: to prepare you for activity. There are three exceptions to the rule. You can meditate longer if you're sick (because it will help speed your recovery); if you're pregnant (you're theoretically meditating for two); or if you're in a residence course under the supervision of TM teachers.

When I think of transcendental meditation I think of the Beatles and Mia Farrow. What was their connection?

The Beatles first heard the Maharishi speak in London in the summer of 1967 and were immediately taken with him. The week after the lecture they were initiated and became outspoken proponents of TM. They announced that they had given up drugs because they had finally found something meaningful. The following winter all four Beatles traveled with their wives and girl friends to the Maharishi's ashram (meditation center) at Rishikesh, India. Ringo Starr left after ten days, comparing the center to an English day school and saying, "I wouldn't want anyone to think I didn't like it there, but I missed my children." The other Beatles stayed on in India and continued to attract a great deal of publicity to the movement.

This publicity brought others to the Maharishi's side: singer Donovan, Mick Jagger and the Rolling Stones, the Jefferson Airplane, most of the members of the Doors, actress Shirley MacLaine, and the Beach Boys. Mia Farrow left her husband, Frank Sinatra, and went to India at the request of her younger sister (who is now a TM instructor in Boston), but departed shortly after arriving, saying "I went with the Maharishi because I couldn't find solace in the materialistic world—and it [Rishikesh] was like a movie set."

The bubble burst when the Maharishi scheduled a tour of the United States with the Beach Boys. The Beatles came out from under his wing, claiming a firm belief in TM and a great deal of disappointment in what they considered to be the relatively materialistic attitudes of the Maharishi. The tour was a monumental failure and was halted after the first few concerts. Slowly, the famous stars, transcendental meditation, and the Maharishi faded from the headlines. But many of the famous continued to meditate, including three of the Beatles. On an interview show in New York late in 1971, George Harrison said, "Transcendental meditation is fantastic," and said that meditation made him feel as if he was on a boat riding smoothly at anchor over gentle waves. Television star Efrem Zimbalist, Jr., recently revealed that he has been meditating, with wonderful results, for the last five years.

The era of the Beatles is regarded with mixed feelings by those inside the movement. There is no doubt that TM received its first major exposure because of the Beatles, but the exposure had both positive and negative results. On the minus side of the ledger was the fact that many scientists who had been interested in investigating certain phenomena changed their minds, and only after the turn of the decade began a return to the subject. Also, the fact that the Beatles seemed to drop in and drop out so quickly caused many people to dismiss TM as a fad. On the positive side, the interest of the Beatles made the movement well known, and there is no telling how many people were eventually drawn to try meditation because of that exposure.

Isn't transcendental meditation a lot of hokum and a soon-to-be-forgotten fad?

"There has been a vast amount of empirical and scientific evidence concerning TM, and there can no longer be any doubt about the value of this technique," says a New York educator. "Transcendental meditation brings about a unique state of consciousness and has positively affected tens of thousands of people."

The movement also has not had the quick rise in popularity normally associated with fads. TM began growing in the United States in 1961 and, except for 1968, when the interest of the Beatles spurred a minor jump in memberships, has recorded a steady growth pattern. The fact that no follow-up surveys are made makes it hard to determine how many people continue to meditate after being initiated. In response to the criticism that TM is just a fad, a veteran meditator responded, "TM is not just a fad, because it has its basis in reality. It's not like dying your hair blue or hanging a coonskin tail from your hat. It's not based on an ever-changing climate of acceptance. TM is a state of consciousness that hasn't been widely known previously. Because it's finally getting some attention, people look at it as something strange."

A history professor at an Eastern Ivy League college looked at it as more than strange. He thought it was fraudulent, and began investigating it with the express purpose of exposing TM to the world as phony. Instead he found, "To my dismay, I couldn't dismiss it at all. It works, I don't know how it works, but it works. In my case it had a curious effect—I used to smoke more than two packs of cigarettes a day. Now I've cut it out completely."

I've been told that the Maharishi is just out to make a pile of money. Honestly, isn't that so?

There has been much skepticism surrounding TM and its leading exponent, Maharishi Mahesh Yogi, and it has come from many sources.

A respected British author, Peregrine Worsthorne, is one source of criticism: "His message does seem rather preposterous and, to my mind, almost puerile. I do not for a moment suggest that the Maharishi has anything earth-shaking to offer."

Martin Ebon, in his book, *Maharishi, the Guru,* reports: "The Maharishi has been sharply criticized by other Indian sages, who complain his program of spiritual peace without either penance or asceticism contravenes every traditional Hindu belief. His detractors are also upset by the Maharishi's claim that the *Bhagavad Gita*, Hinduism's epic religious poem, has been wrongly interpreted by most previous commentators."

The Maharishi has been severely criticized by people who resent his apparent fondness for publicity. Ebon notes, "His rivals, quite naturally, speak of him as a charlatan, suggesting that his background does not qualify him as a 'guru' or spiritual teacher, or that he has betrayed vital principles of yoga in particular and Hinduism in general."

The Maharishi has repeatedly stated, "I have nothing. I am a monk. I deal in wisdom and not in money."

A U.S. government investigator said, *"No one seems to be making a financial profit from the movement. It certainly isn't a 'get-rich-quick' outfit!"*

Can a confirmed skeptic benefit from TM?

Yes. The practice of TM has been criticized mostly for the ease with which it is learned. In contrast to the years that must be spent to master other Eastern religious disciplines and yoga, which offer the same results that TM proponents claim, teachers say TM can be taught in a matter of minutes. The fact that it is so easy to learn has made it difficult to accept.

"I can understand the skepticism," a SIMS coordinator commented. "In this age we've been bombarded with so many promises and so few results. I can't blame people for being skeptical. A few years ago we were being told that LSD was the greatest thing that ever happened to mankind.

"There's little doubt that most people are more

127

than a little wary when they first come here. No one likes to be made a fool of. But if someone follows the directions of his teacher, his skepticism will have to disappear. The experience you gain from meditating comes irrespective of belief. Faith doesn't enhance it and skepticism doesn't reduce it."

TM leaders usually answer skeptics by quoting a former skeptic who is currently involved in TM. This summation of the state of TM came from author James Crenshaw in an article entitled, "The Hippies: Beyond Pot and LSD." A former drug user and member of a hippie commune told Crenshaw, "Generally, the family concluded that the system works, and it works very meaningfully, and that the man himself [Maharishi] is just an ordinary man. *He is no mahatma . . . but his system works beautifully!*"

Will transcendental meditation benefit my body?

More scientific work has been done to answer this question than any other, and it can be stated with authority that during meditation the body goes into a physiologically unique state, unlike any of the other three known states of consciousness (waking, sleeping, dreaming). During meditation, the body consumes less oxygen, eliminates less carbon dioxide, and the heart rate, cardiac output, and respiratory rate decrease significantly. Skin resistance, one of the body's means of indicating relaxation, increases greatly. Overall, the metabolic rate of the body is reduced 20 percent.

Much of this physical evidence is similar to what is observable when an individual is sleeping, but brain tests by electroencephalograph (EEG) show that the mind is not asleep during meditation, but, rather, fully awake and able to respond to stimuli. The combined physical and mental states are unlike anything previously known and indicate the existence of a fourth major state of consciousness.

The first major study of physical changes in the body during meditation was made in 1970 by Dr. Keith Wallace, then at the department of physiology of the University of California, Los Angeles. Dr. Wallace's study was entitled, "The Physiological Effects of Transcendental Meditation." He used twenty-seven subjects and tested their oxygen consumption, carbon-dioxide-release rate, cardiac output, blood pressure, heart rate, skin resistance, and brain wave patterns while meditating. His results proved to be the first conclusive evidence that TM does produce this fourth state:

> Within five to ten minutes after the onset of meditation, the doctor wrote O_2 (oxygen) consumption and CO_2 (carbon dioxide) elimination decreased significantly in all subjects measured . . . therefore there was a decrease in the metabolic rate.

Dr. Wallace then discussed the sleeping states that produce similar results. Tests of that state proved important, he continued, because they pointed out that

> whatever processes cause the gradual decrease in O_2 consumption seen during sleep, they seem to be different from the processes which cause the marked decrease in O_2 consumption after only 10 minutes of transcendental meditation.

During meditation there is a mean decrease in cardiac output of about 25%. Grollman (1939) reports that during sleep there is a mean decrease in cardiac output of about 20%.

The slight decrease of arterial pH and the significant decrease of base excess during transcendental meditation indicates a change in the acid-base balance of the body . . . Epinephrine is known to cause anxiety symptoms. [It] seems plausible that the decreased arterial lactate concentration during TM might be caused by decreased production of epinephrine.

This last is important because it indicates that there is less excretion of the chemical that seems to appear in the body during times of stress.

Dr. Wallace continued:

During meditation there is a significant mean decrease in heart rate of 5 beats/min. During sleep the mean decrease varies with each investigator ranging from one to two beats up to a dozen or more per minute. The changes in heart rate, blood pressure, and skin resistance during meditation all suggest specific changes within the functioning of the autonomic nervous system.

In other words, the body undergoes important physiological changes during meditation.

As for mental changes, "The EEG patterns seen during TM clearly distinguish the transcendental state from sleep and dreaming." Wallace summed up his report by saying:

The significant and rapid reduction of oxygen consumption, heart rate, and cardiac output and the marked rise in skin resistance indicate that within a few minutes transcendental meditation produces a deep state of rest and relaxation. The changes in blood gases suggest that the state of rest is accompanied by biochemical changes.

Working independently in London, Dr. John Allison discovered even more profound changes in his subjects. Dr. Allison found that during meditation "the changes at the beginning and end of meditation are immediate; the rate of respiration is about half the resting rate, and after meditation stops the rate returns at once to premeditation levels. [It] is clear from these results," Dr. Allison wrote, "that a profound change in physiological events accompanies this simple mental activity."

Sidney Scott, writing in the *Mensa Journal* reported on the Allison tests:

> The significance of the physiological effects is twofold: the body is allowed a new kind of rest, and clearly the effects are not trivial; for example, in the view of Allison's commentator, the new level of oxygen intake would usually be taken as incompatible with the maintenance of life.

Finally Dr. Herbert Benson, an internist and cardiologist who specializes in hypertension who had been testing meditators at Harvard Medical School, joined forces with Dr. Wallace. The result of their efforts was published by the *American Journal of Physiology*. This report was summed up by *Time* magazine as follows:

> (T)he metabolic rate of meditators decreased significantly. The heart pumped less, the electrical

resistance of the skin, an indication of emotion
tension, increased markedly, showing the meditator was relaxed; and his body produced smaller
amounts of carbon dioxide. The brain alpha
waves increased in intensity—another sign of
relaxation—while less lactic acid was produced
in the blood, a possible indication of reduced
anxiety.

Drs. Benson and Wallace later showed that after fifteen minutes of meditation an individual's oxygen
metabolism was reduced to a level that normally took
six hours of sleep to achieve.

The results of the Wallace-Allison-Benson work
has spurred a number of other investigations. Researchers at the University of Texas found that, after
meditation, an individual's reaction time decreased 12
percent—while the reaction time of the control group,
whose members just sat quietly with their eyes closed
for twenty minutes, increased about ten percent.
Another survey showed that the behavior patterns of
meditators was markedly superior to their nonmedi-
tating peers in terms of social compatibility, happiness, and acceptance of problems.

Other studies are beginning to cover a wide area.
There have been numerous reports from meditators
that their eye sight has improved, although there does
not seem to be a medical reason for this. Artists note
that they seem to be able to work faster and on a
higher creative level. And even athletes are beginning
to experiment with TM: two Chicago Bears football
players have become meditators. The drug studies
have been discussed previously.

There can be no doubt that transcendental meditation produces a state of consciousness unlike any-

thing we've known before, and closest to that state of Zen developed after many years of intense study. Practical applications range from treating sickness, shortening postoperative recovery time, and in Dr. Wallace's words, TM might even "be applied in space travel where extended periods of low oxygen consumption simultaneous with responsive mental activity would be useful."

Some maintain that they have had problems since starting TM. One of the critical articles about the method appeared in the German magazine, *Der Spiegel*. "The people who teach TM," writer Peter Brügge said "are actually amateur spiritual doctors and really have no idea of how to deal with emotional problems."

Seven months after he began meditation, Brügge claimed, he couldn't sleep at night, had become extremely sensitive to the sun, was so nervous that he couldn't work, heard noises, began to dislike music he once liked, and felt complete inability to cope with the problems around him.

He also said that meditation had caused a young female meditator in Germany to get migraine headaches; a young man to suffer his first epileptic fit; and a housewife to seek psychiatric care.

In the extensive research required for this book, the authors found no evidence that TM caused problems of the magnitude Brügge described.

Eastern philosophy seems to be the "in" thing. How long has it had followers in the United States?

America's first real contact with Eastern philosophy came in 1893 when Swami Vivekananda came to speak at the World's Parliament of Religions in Chicago. Vivekananda was good looking, witty, gentle, and calm, so he attracted a great deal of attention. He took advantage of it by founding the American Vedanta Society—the first official Hindu center in the United States.

It wasn't until 1920 that the "second wave" arrived. Swami Yogananda, who was backed by a prince from India, arrived to lecture at the Pilgrim Tercentenary Anniversary International Congress of Religious Liberals in Boston. After the conclusion of the congress, the swami went to California and founded the Yogoda Sat-Sanga Movement. It has been estimated that this movement had a membership of over 25,000 by 1930. The boom had begun. Nearly one hundred similar organizations, many of them run by phony swamis, opened across the country. This fad died a quiet death just before World War II.

After the war, there was renewed interest in Eastern philosophy, particularly in Zen Buddhism, which J.D. Salinger popularized in his short stories. Yoga became permanently entrenched in America, and yoga institutes, some of them still open and prospering, opened. After a leveling-off period in the 1950s, the growth of "spiritual" centers began booming again in the 1960s.

With the possible exception of transcendental meditation, the best known movement is Bhakti Yoga, or "The Yoga of Ecstasy." Members of this group have attracted attention to it by wearing long robes, shaving their heads (except for a pigtail in the back) and marching around many U.S. cities singing the simple *"Hare Krishna,"* which is translated to mean "hail to God."

Transcendental meditation, which differs from all others in technique, if not in goal, is probably the most successful of the Americanized Eastern philosophies. Because it can be learned quickly and will yield immediate results, TM has grown and prospered since 1961. In a single decade, more than 100,000 people have been initiated, far more than have ever been involved in any other discipline from the East.

Isn't TM the same thing as self-hypnosis, concentration, and contemplation?

TM differs from all other processes, of which autohypnosis, concentration, and contemplation are but three examples, in technique and physiological results, although the state of the mind during meditation may be somewhat similar.

The difference between TM and autohypnosis (or autosuggestion) has been shown scientifically. Dr. R. Keith Wallace, in his study, summed up all his test results and then said, "These results distinguish the state produced by TM from commonly encountered states of consciousness . . . and altered states such as hypnosis and conditioning." During hypnotic sleep, Dr. Wallace noted, there is no noticeable change in oxygen consumption, even when the subject is in a state of complete relaxation. Wallace conducted other, similar tests to confirm the fact that TM is unlike any form of hypnosis. Actually, all he would have had to do was ask the Maharishi, who has his own explanation:

"I am told," he said, "that in hypnosis a man falls into a state which doesn't belong to him in reality. The poor man thinks, 'I am rich, I am rich,' and then he begins to feel the wealth, but it is only superficial, it is not in reality. The hypnotic state brings the mind to a state which is unreal and makes man completely unrealistic."

When asked how TM differed from concentration,

the Maharishi had a quick answer. "In concentration the mind is fixed. It doesn't move and it must be free to move." Using one of his for-every-occasion analogies, he continued, "If you want to keep a dog in a corner you can either tie it with a chain (concentration) or feed it so as to make it like the corner (meditation). The mind should not be tied. It should be allowed to wander freely and that is because man's basic instinct gives him a motivation toward happiness." Concentration, in other words, involves fixing the mind on a certain point. TM allows the mind to pick its own points, or pick no points at all.

Contemplation involves focusing attention on one specific thought, or thing, and considering it in all its states. Again, the mind must be controlled during contemplation. During transcendental meditation there is no attempt to control or focus the mind. If, for example, a song the meditator likes is playing in the next room, his mind is free to wander and focus on that song. This would not be so during either contemplation or concentration.

How does transcendental meditation differ from other types of meditation?

Transcendental meditation differs from all other meditation techniques not in goal, but in the best method of getting there. Most other meditations involve suggestion, control, belief, intellectual understanding, concentration, contemplation, faith that the system will work—and a change in life style. TM involves none of these. It uses the natural tendency of the mind to wander deeper and deeper into consciousness until it theoretically arrives at the source of thought.

The physiological evidence that TM differs from other types of meditation centers on the Wallace tests.

The only previously recorded EEG patterns (brain waves) that are at all similar to those recorded by TM subjects, have come from expert Zen monks and yogis. These people, however, managed to produce these patterns *only after twenty years of meditative experience, while some of Wallace's subjects had as little as two months of TM training.*

Dr. Wallace summed up the differences between TM and other types of meditation in his study.

A common goal of most systems of meditation is the realization of the essential constituent of creation. Although this goal has many names . . . most systems agree that it takes years of difficult discipline and training to attain this goal. Maharishi, however, states that the attainment of this goal is easy, natural and accomplished automatically with the practice of TM . . . He says that just as there are physiological changes which occur during waking, sleeping, and dreaming state of consciousness, there are physiological changes which occur during the transcendental state. This concept is supported by the evidence given in this study.

The difference between TM and other styles of meditation also emerges in the reaction of most other Indian meditators toward Maharishi. He is unpopular and his system is deemed fraudulent. An Indian critic of TM told a reporter for *The New York Times:* "It is a cause of self-survival and very necessary that we attack any meditation technique offering 'instant results.' If not, our disciples will soon start attacking us and vanishing completely." Most of the hundreds of Indian ashrams (places where meditation is taught) are open only to those disciples willing to commit themselves to spending a minimum of two years, and in these centers Westerners are expected to learn the prevailing language and the local dialect.

Is TM just another form of yoga?

No. The basic goals of yoga and TM—to reach a state of bliss consciousness and total fulfillment—are the same, but the methods and results are different. The Maharishi explained the difference by noting, "TM works on the natural tendency of the mind; the other works by training the mind to focus elsewhere. The tendency of the mind is to grow, to advance. This is quite enough to take it to unbounded awareness. That is why no effort, or control is involved."

Webster's Seventh Collegiate Dictionary makes the same point, defining yoga as a philosophy that teaches "the suppression of all activity of the body, mind and will in order that the self may realize its distinction from them and attain liberation." By contrast, there is no suppression of any kind in TM. The body is left to relax. The mind and will are left to focus on whatever strikes their fancy; whatever drifts or pops into the mind during transcendental meditation is welcome.

Yoga is also a much more involved process. It can be described as a complete program consisting of many parts. TM, on the other hand, is a complete program consisting of only one part: meditation. In some advanced stages of TM the basic yoga positions are taught, but only if the meditator is interested in learning them. A very large percentage of meditators never learns anything about yoga. True yoga, incidentally, involves an ascetic life style and extensive preparations. *TM involves neither.*

The Maharishi further explained, "Many forms of yoga have been practiced. These methods have, however, always been for the recluse who lives apart from society and remains almost unaffected by the fate of the vast majority of householders. Today the householder is offered a simple method of deep meditation that is just as effective as that practiced by the recluse in his seclusion."

Where does one meditate?

Since the only equipment needed to meditate successfully is your body, you can meditate almost anywhere. The only restrictions are that you should be somewhat comfortable and in a place where you'll be as uninterrupted as possible. If you're meditating at home, it is suggested that you take the phone off the hook and place animals behind a closed door. Many people meditate on the way to work, in the office, or in a plane. One vigorous young man claims he meditated successfully while floating on his back in a swimming pool.

The first place where you'll meditate is also where you're initiated and that could be in any of the 50 states or in 51 other nations. TM is particularly strong in England, West Germany, Norway, and Sweden. It is growing rapidly in many other countries. You can secure lists of centers by writing:

SIMS National Coordinating Center
1015 Gayley Avenue
Los Angeles, California 90024

International Meditation Society
1015 Gayley Avenue
Los Angeles, California 90024

Spiritual Regeneration Movement
11428 Santa Monica Boulevard
Los Angeles, California 90025

How much is it going to cost me to join? And who gets the money?

Adults pay $75, students $35, for the four sessions required to learn how to meditate. This fee covers all lectures, checking, and permanent use of facilities at any center. Advanced TM techniques, which an individual can choose to learn after a minimum of two years' meditation, may require a slight additional fee.

SIMS and all related groups are nonprofit organizations, but each new initiate is asked to pay the basic fee. The funds thus gathered are used to maintain the centers and provide living expenses for teachers (which rarely exceeds $250 monthly. Many of the teachers have other employment and donate their services.)

"During his first world tour," Jerry Jarvis relates, "the Maharishi asked for no donations. He discovered to his dismay that the people who were instructed in the technique of transcendental meditation treated it as though someone had placed diamonds around their necks; but, not knowing the value, they discarded them as though they were merely rocks. When Maharishi was told that people in the West equated everything according to its monetary value, and that a week's net income would enable people to place the true value of what they had been given, he reluctantly agreed to the payments." The initiation fee was the equivalent of one week of an initiate's salary through most of 1966 when it was changed to the present rates.

But the price list contains special "bargains." A married couple, and all their children under 15 who are not full time students, are charged a total of $125. Children are asked to contribute a week's allowance or, if that isn't possible, to agree to do chores around their own house for a week.

"No one is making any money from TM," an official said, "and we never turn anyone away who can't afford to start. All we're asking is that TM become important enough to make an effort, to make an effort, to make it have meaning. We do ask that everyone give something, even those who can't possibly afford the initiation fee. We ask for some type of token donation, even if it's only a dollar."

The cost of the teacher training course varies depending on where the instruction is to be given, as fees go to pay for accommodations. It usually averages out to about $50 weekly. Residence courses cost roughly the same, although SIMS centers do pick up some of the expenses for the teachers.

What's so special about a TM teacher?

Every teaching applicant is carefully screened to determine how sincere he is about his decision to go into teaching. This screening process eliminates those who lack the ability to teach.

TM teachers undergo a special three-month course (the last two months being taught by the Maharishi) that enables them to impart the system to other people. The program begins with a one-month course, most often given in the individual's own country. After that the two-month follow-up is given wherever suitable accommodations are available.

The course is not very difficult. It involves memorization and testing, more on philosophical matters than facts, and consists mostly of lectures and meditations. There is extensive training in verifying an individual's own TM experiences, and practice in initiating new meditators. A deeper understanding of the concepts behind transcendental meditation is also encouraged.

The work is usually done in groups. The Maharishi does most of the lecturing and there is a question-and-answer session at the end of each lecture. Teachers-in-training wear regular clothes and there is very little socializing. To keep expenses down, very few meat meals are served, but even so the program costs about $50 per week. An individual qualifies as an instructor competent to teach TM "when the Maharishi pronounces you ready." This is usually at the end of the three-month period. The Maharishi gives each individual his or her final lesson privately.

At the end of 1971 there were more than 2,000 teachers of TM in the world, half of them in the United States. This number was expected to double in the following eighteen months.

TM teachers have varied backgrounds. Stockbrokers, housewives, lawyers, secretaries, students, storekeepers, and engineers manage to combine teaching TM with their regular occupations.

I'm in my fourth month of pregnancy; what effect will transcendental meditation have on my baby?

Meditation during pregnancy is highly recommended. The deep rest provided by TM is particularly advantageous for mothers-to-be, and an unofficial survey showed that a large number of female meditators have had extremely easy, natural childbirth. The babies are found to be more alert from the moment of birth and develop their motor skills quite early, although there is as yet no medical evidence to support this. However, the staff members of a New York hospital were so impressed by the response of a baby born to a meditator mother that they requested a series of TM lectures be given in the hospital.

A Dayton woman learned to meditate after her child had been conceived. She meditated during the birth of the baby and caused her doctor to remark that hers was the easiest childbirth he had ever witnessed.

Another meditator traveled to Mallorca, Spain, and became a teacher of TM while she was pregnant. "This was the most beautiful thing that ever happened to me," she said. "As I meditated, my entire system got deep rest and relaxation—and my baby got this, too. I had a natural childbirth. The nurses said they had never seen a baby that was as alert as quickly as mine. I recommend meditation to anyone who is even thinking of having a baby!"

Is TM a substitute for sleep?

No. If your body and mind are tired when you sit down to meditate, chances are you'll fall fast asleep during your meditation. Although TM does provide a deeper level of rest than a full night's sleep, it cannot provide the prolonged physical rest your body needs. It can, and does, act much like a pep pill, though. If you haven't had enough sleep, and you then meditate, you will feel more rested and aware than you normally would.

If it's not a substitute for sleep, is it a cure for insomnia?

It may be, depending on what is causing your insomnia. If insomnia is due to a build-up of stress in your system, as much insomnia is, and you find yourself tossing and turning all night, then TM will probably act as a cure. A New Jersey bank teller had tried everything to get to sleep: warm milk, reading, a game of Jotto, counting sheep, cows, and pigeons. Even the "Late Late Show" wouldn't put her to sleep. Then she began meditating. Now she complains of another problem: She sleeps so soundly she doesn't hear her alarm clock going off.

Most people do report changes in sleeping habits after beginning to meditate. If they have been sleeping more than they like, they tend to sleep less; if they were waking earlier than they wish to, then TM seems to help them sleep much deeper, and longer.

Do you have to change your life style when you become a meditator?

No. This has been a source of both criticism and attraction for the movement. Leaders of other disciplines, as well as people who have investigated other Eastern philosophies, claim that any method that does not involve a complete change in an individual's life style is worthless. TM teachers dispute this, insisting that TM is a practical technique that is not influenced by an individual's way of living.

This has made TM particularly attractive to Americans. TM, in fact, almost seems to have been tailored for the American way of life. "TM may be practiced by any normal person, whatever his life may be," the Maharishi says. "It is not just for the naturally contemplative man, but particularly for the busy, active man, the householder with his commitments and responsibilities . . . He sits down in the morning . . . and then he takes up the activity of the day in an ordinary way. He is called upon to do nothing else. He need believe nothing, he need think nothing and he need do nothing he is not already doing. He leads a normal, practical life as he did before.

"Once we start restricting, that is an obstacle to progress. We say, very well, go ahead with your outer life as much as you want; enjoy, bring fulfillment to yourself on all levels of consciousness. We don't restrict outside activity. Only we anchor it, so that it remains stable, so stable that it gives more encouragement, more energy, more intelligence to bring fulfillment to a much deeper degree."

Even though TM has been compared to brushing one's teeth ("You just add it to your routine because it's good for you"), it still may change your life style. In numerous cases people have drastically altered their way of existence after beginning to meditate.

"When I began TM I was goofing off," a twenty-four-year-old student said, "I was flunking out of school and taking drugs. I felt far out, and my only interest was in getting farther out. I am now preparing to begin teaching junior high school. I am a respected, responsible member of society. Meditation has transformed virtually every area of my life."

One of the life-style changes that seems to appear with some regularity is a change in diet, although this is a purely voluntary decision. *Many meditators find themselves eating less.* Others find themselves switching to health foods or beginning a vegetarian existence. To generalize, although TM does not call for any change in an individual's life style, purely voluntary changes that lead to a healthier state of mind do occur.

What does all this mean in terms of general health?
Will meditating make me healthier?

Statistics prove that it probably will. Studies done thus far indicate that transcendental meditation has a definite impact on an individual's health. The Maharishi says, "When we give rest to the machinery, working all the time inside, then it has less chance of getting diseases." His basic reasoning is excellent.

Medical science has long agreed that deep rest is important to the system, and rest may act as a cure in certain situations. TM, as the Benson-Wallace studies showed, provides large amounts of extra, deep rest.

In the conclusion of his study, Dr. Wallace commented, "Various techniques of meditation and yoga exercise for treatment of physical and mental disorders have been applied for many thousands of years. The use of these techniques is very limited due to the difficulty of the discipline and the time required to achieve beneficial results." Dr. Wallace suggested that, besides reducing physical and mental tension (both contributors to poor health), TM might also help control blood pressure and aid in disease where low oxygen consumption and improved mental activity could combine to improve a patient's condition.

He verified his theory with a survey. Of three hundred ninety-four subjects who answered his query, 67 percent reported significant improvement in physical health, 31 percent reported no significant changes, and 2 percent reported an increase in sickness. An even more impressive 84 percent reported significant improvement in their mental health (16 percent reported no change in their mental condition). In most cases, when a subject reported there had been no significant change in his physical or mental health he would also report that he had been in good health before beginning meditation and continued to be in good health.

Of the 67 percent who improved—the two hundred sixty-seven subjects who noticed significant *physical* changes—7 subjects found that their high blood pressure condition had either improved or disappeared, 3 noted that their ulcers improved, 5 mentioned an improvement of their asthma, 19 noticed a decrease in allergies, 29 had fewer headaches, 117 had fewer colds, and 7 found improvement in areas ranging from acne to weight loss.

Of the three hundred thirty-three subjects—or 84 percent—who reported improvement in their *mental* health, 22 dropped regular psychiatric treatment because of TM, and 25 mentioned less depression and fewer suicidal tendencies.

There is a great deal of hope that TM will prove to be beneficial in the treatment of heart disease. Although tests are scheduled, there is as yet no proof that TM can help heart-disease victims. But a number of cardiologists, among them Harvard's Dr. Herbert Benson, may often recommend TM to patients with a heart problem. The theory is that many attacks are brought on by continued stress, and since TM has been effective in relieving stress it therefore should be useful to heart patients.

A professor of physics at Princeton University says: "There is no doubt that TM improves your general health. It is not a cure all. It is not a magic potion. TM is simply a method that acts to relieve stress and provide deep rest. In that way, transcendental meditation can be extremely beneficial to your health."

What is TM's future?

Transcendental meditation has been referred to as the wave of the future. SIMS officials predict that, within a few years, men, women, and children throughout the world will have the opportunity to become meditators. Not just individuals, but large groups are also expected to become involved. In this country, corporations, schools, the military, drug-control centers, prisons, hospitals, and even athletic teams are currently trying TM or are about to embark upon meditation programs.

Certainly it is no cure-all. Last season, the exasperated manager of a semipro baseball team watched his club drop seven games in a row. He tried frantically to reverse the losing streak with rabbits' feet and four-leaf clovers. Nothing worked. Finally, in desperation, he took the advice of his wife, a meditator, and had a teacher of TM instruct his players in the method. After the final lecture the members of the now happily meditating team announced resolutely that they were ready for all opponents. They lost their remaining four games, finishing securely in last place.

Still elated, they said with determination "Just wait till next year!", thereby showing that most people can be meditators but that even massive infusions of tranquility and energy need not produce expert baseball players.

TM does not pretend to be a panacea. However, there is solid evidence that TM helps reduce or eliminate tension; expands the mind; develops man's creative intelligence; and makes use of his full potential.

The Maharishi might have had determined meditators like the baseball players in mind when he said, "Wonderful things can occur in the future, but man must come to realize that even if he cannot always win the contest, he is still born with the ability to enjoy it."

Enjoy!

7

The Authors Talk About Their TM Experiences

Jhan Robbins:

Hollywood no longer portrays the working journalist as a hat-wearing, chain-smoking, hard-drinking chap. But the movie-makers still feel it essential to cast him as a cynical fellow, and I guess I conform to that impression. Over the years of pursuing my profession, some of the very best con artists have tried to convince me that their product was A number 1. Out of necessity, I've had to take precautions. My nose always comes to my rescue and the moment it starts twitching I become wary.

In the Soviet Union I talked to Boris Pasternak, author of *Dr. Zhivago*, shortly before his death. The Russian writer who became somewhat suspect in Western eyes when he refused the Nobel prize in literature, gave me his last message to the world. When I was ready to publish the statement, super-suspicious Soviet "experts" told me that the message was all part of a Soviet propaganda plot. *My nose twitched.* I didn't believe the experts, and I was right.

Sitting in a silver-gilt chair, Emperor Haile Selassie of Ethiopia assured me that his royal lion was so tame that I could safely put my head in its mouth. *My nose twitched,* and I've always been glad that it did.

Once in Vietnam, I was captured by the Vietcong. An enemy major kept telling me that I had nothing to worry about. *My nose twitched,* although I was eventually released without harm.

When I was asked to write about transcendental meditation, my nose again began to twitch. To say that I was dubious would only be a half-truth. Although I meditated in Quaker Meeting, I was more disbelieving about TM than the most conservative inhabitant of Missouri, the show-me state.

I credit a homemade silk tie for the loss of my first measure of skepticism. The tie was to be a Christmas present, and it had been created by a woman who meditated. She told me that she had always bought her presents, but this year she decided to make them by hand.

"I can't think of anything else that has given me as much energy as TM," she said. "I find myself doing so many things I never did before—painting, cooking, sewing. It has to come from some place and my guess is TM." Earlier that day I had talked to one of her friends and learned that this hadn't always been her way.

"I suppose she was okay," said her friend. "But she wasn't the kind to give you the shirt off her back. Not even one of the buttons. Now, since this meditating stuff, she can't do enough for you."

My next interview put another notch in the skepticism. This time the meditator was a tugboat captain.

I was a little early and he hadn't arrived as yet. I talked to one of his mates. "He was a real Captain Bligh," I was told. "I've been working under him for seven years and for six of them he never asked me how I was or wanted to know anything about my family. I don't even think he knew I had a family. But all that was before he began to meditate a year ago."

Just then the captain arrived. He was all smiles, nodded to the mate, inquired as to his health and the health of his family. He called each by name. The mate couldn't resist whispering, "See what I mean?"

For the most part, I got the same results from the other people I interviewed. They seemed to be decent and kind. I pride myself on my ability to spot a phony. They weren't! Oh, sure, I ran into some creeps, but they were definitely in the minority. One of them even apologized for his behavior.

"I missed meditating this morning," he explained sadly.

I'm sure my collaborator, Dave Fisher, could detect the days when I missed meditating, and I believe I always knew the times he was too busy to practice TM. We talked to many members of SIMS; they answered our questions fully, never dodging one. They didn't try to hide anything and made all their records available to us. Perhaps they could fool one reporter, but I don't think two of them.

I must admit that I learned how to meditate because of the book. I wanted to know more about the procedure, but along the way I found myself getting very serious about it. I'm glad I did, and I would recommend it to my friends.

What benefits have I received from meditating? Quite a few.

Previously, my working span at the typewriter

was comparatively brief. I would constantly try to find excuses to leave it, making an "important" telephone call, suddenly feeling very hungry, mailing an "urgent" letter, viewing a "very necessary" television show. I now can write for hours at a time, and editors seem to think the results are good.

I sleep less than before, yet I feel more rested. I remember my dreams now, and they are in color.

Before, my mind and desk used to be cluttered with loads of useless items. My mind seems to have cleared up (but I still have piles of junk next to my typewriter).

I used to get headaches. I haven't had one since I started meditating. That's not quite true. I had a headache the second day I meditated. But after meditation, it disappeared and hasn't returned.

I find I have become more of an optimist. Formerly, I did look at some things with a degree of pessimism. That, too, has vanished. Occasionally, this goes a little too far. Last week a waitress stained my jacket when she overturned her tray full of blueberry pies. I told her not to fret about it—cleaning would get it out. It didn't.

Despite the stain on my jacket, I've become a meditating name-dropper. I discuss it often. Recently I ran into an old gym teacher I had in high school, and he repeated a slogan he used to quote in class, "A healthy *mind* in a healthy *body* is the best you can hope for."

I told him that I thought I had found something that provides both: transcendental meditation.

David Fisher:

I have a great fascination with the unusual, which is one of the major reasons I've always wanted to be

a writer. And in the years that I've been writing pro-
fessionally, I've covered as many new and different
territories as I'd hoped for. I've written a biography
of Malcolm X, a humor novel, and a how-to-pitch
book with baseball star Ferguson Jenkins. I've written
jokes for a top comedian, speeches for the director of a
national trade association, articles for half a dozen
magazines, and even a promotional pamphlet for a
flavor-making company.

In my capacity as a reporter for *Life* magazine,
I've traveled all over the country—from a Los Angeles
courtroom to an aged farm neatly tucked deep on a
Louisiana bayou. I've met people ranging from Mu-
hammad Ali to a German immigrant who still spoke
no English but who remembers her trip to America in
1904—costing less than $50.

Then Jhan Robbins called.

"You know something about transcendental meditation, don't you?" he asked.

I did know the basic facts about TM—and had
to admit being somewhat dubious about the claims
I had heard meditators make. I filled Jhan in with
what I knew, and he explained that a publisher had
asked if he was interested in doing a book on the
subject. We decided to do some background research
and see if there was enough legitimate material to
support a worthwhile book. We spent the next few
months going through research data and talking to
scientists, and finally to meditators. My skepticism
hadn't disappeared, I just put it away while I tried
to assume an unbiased, open position on the subject.

Jhan and I began this book by spending a full
afternoon with the New York SIMS director, Jack
Forem. What initially amazed me about Jack, and
about every other meditator I was to meet in the

ensuing months, was his openness and friendliness. In fact, for awhile we toyed with the idea of naming this book *The Constant Smile*, because that phrase most accurately described the people we met.

Even though I was determined to keep an open mind, I had formed a picture of what I expected the typical meditator to be like. I had more or less expected to meet people who couldn't prosper in open society and had turned to TM as others turn to the vast number of flourishing cults throughout the country—people who had banded together because they craved companionship.

I couldn't have been more wrong.

The people we met during our research covered every conceivable age, sex, religious, ethnic, social, and racial group. There were pretty girls and plain ones, sanitation workers and army generals, teen-agers and septuagenarians.

So the people in TM were quite a bit different from what I suspected. No fanatics. This was the beginning of the end of some of my skepticism. But I still was determined to keep my reportorial distance. Jhan and I decided we would be initiated, but I have to admit I personally did not expect to gain anything from the technique. Listening to the two introductory lectures convinced me I must be right. Much of it seemed to be gobbledy-gook. It didn't seem to make any sense at all. I felt extremely ridiculous walking to the SIMS center, fruit, flowers, and handkerchief in hand, when the time came for me to be initiated. My only hope was that I would not be seen by someone who knew me.

I meditated for the first time during my initiation and was amazed. I mean, really surprised! Physically, I felt a wave of relaxation surging through my body.

My shoulders sagged and I was completely relaxed. Totally. I felt as if I had taken a step away from the everyday world. More skepticism shattered.

That night I meditated for the second time, now away from the center, away from the warmth and the incense and the comfortable chairs. I felt ridiculous sitting down and repeating a sound that made no sense at all, over and over in my mind.

All the skepticism that I had retained concerning the physical value of the technique ceased that night. There was no doubt in my mind that the process did everything that Jack Forem and other TM advocates had promised. But my doubts concerning the Maharishi remained. I made it a point then, and still do, of referring to him, in the more formal style, as "the Maharishi," not by first name, ("Maharishi says . . ."), which most other meditators use.

As I continued working on this book, I began to look forward to my daily meditations. In the morning I made sure I left myself plenty of time to meditate before leaving my apartment. At night I would put off meditating until I had finished everything I had to do and used TM as a reward. Although I didn't always have the same reaction as on that first day, the relaxation I still receive from TM far exceeds anything I could have imagined previously.

When I began meditating, I made a point of not discussing the subject with friends. I was determined to maintain a totally objective position. But when my curious, and somewhat amused, friends kept on asking me how my meditation was going, I stopped resisting. I was sitting in a restaurant when the question was put to me for what must have been the fiftieth time.

I decided the time had come to answer. "Look," I said, "I can't vouch for the Maharishi, and I'm told many things that I'm not sure I believe, nor will I say that TM will cure all your problems—but I've already gotten far more out of it than I ever dreamed I would."

"Is it worth the $75 you paid?" my friend asked.

"More!" There went my unbiased stance.

As time passed, I learned more about TM, and many of the mysteries of the first lecture were solved. The strange state of "Being" began to take a misty shape and form. I found the phrase "cosmic consciousness" creeping into my conversations. I even discovered myself becoming defensive when anyone treated the subject with anything less than the seriousness I thought it deserved. I answered critics by quoting statistics from Dr. Benson's surveys or mentioning an anecdote that the impressive General Franklin Davis had related, or telling them about the drug abuser we call T.L.J.

I can't say that all my skepticism is gone. However, most of it has been countered by some of the points made by General Davis or something that someone as respected as Buckminster Fuller says.

I enjoy meeting people involved with TM. The center on Cornelia Street is filled with happy people. There is usually a group in the waiting room, passing time until they are initiated. One of the women I worked with at *Life* told me that her son meditated, and she knew of a group of middle-aged housewives in Boston who were long-time meditators. And I was in a bookstore the other day when the man behind the counter mentioned TM. He was a writer suffering from writer's block—and friends had suggested TM as a cure.

"It's the best thing that ever happened to me,"

he said, "I have more energy than ever before. I was walking down the street yesterday and all of a sudden I had to start running. I had to!"

Nothing as vigorous has happened to me as yet. In fact, when I began I was certain there would be no noticeable changes in my life. But one night I was at a party in Riverdale, N.Y., and the host asked me what I was drinking. "Something soft," I said, an answer that surprised me as much as it did him. I simply had no urge, no need, for a drink. It just didn't appeal to me at all. I've never been a big drinker, but now I very, very rarely have anything except soda and grapefruit juice. The same holds true for marijuana. I never smoked heavily or regularly, but I've only smoked once since I began meditating.

I don't think I've turned into a meditation freak either. I have missed meditating on a number of occasions and every time I did I felt quite guilty about it. The question I still haven't answered is what happens from this page on.

I don't really know. Janet Hoffman, a TM teacher who helped with the preparation of this book, once explained that TM is much like brushing your teeth: once you pick up the habit, it becomes the most natural thing to do.

I like that analogy. TM has become a habit and I do expect to continue. I feel that I am gaining something extra, something I cannot yet describe, something that has yet to manifest itself, from TM.

Do I recommend TM to my friends? Even though I do believe that happy, relaxed people like myself can gain from TM, I always qualify my advice. I tell them that this is a physical process that provides a tremendous amount of relaxation. That it is unbelievably easy to do. That I have met a vast number of impressive meditators during my research. That studies have revealed a new, exciting consciousness with unbounded possibilities. And that I still have doubts about certain things myself. In the end, I point out, they have to make their own decision.

Glossary

Although the reader undoubtedly knows the definitions of many of these words, some of them take on special meanings when used in relation to transcendental meditation. The list was prepared with the cooperation of the Students' International Meditation Society.

ABSOLUTE. A field of energy at the very basis of an object's existence; the nonchanging constant of life. See *Being*.

ALPHA WAVES. Brain-wave patterns associated with restfulness and pleasure. During transcendental meditation the incidence of alpha waves increases, thus suggesting a more relaxed state of wakefulness than normal.

BEING. The essential nature of any object; the basic underlying state of existence. All objects have a state of Being. In TM also known as pure consciousness, transcendental consciousness, absolute, self.

BHAGAVAD GITA. The epic Hindu poem, written more than 5,000 years ago, which discusses the relationship of the individual and this state of Being. Maharishi Mahesh Yogi believes it has been misinterpreted to this point and thus has led to the decay of Indian society.

BLISS CONSCIOUSNESS. The awareness of the full value of existence. See *Being*.

CONCENTRATION. A process of holding the attention on some object or experience. It is not used at all in TM, although it is used in other forms of meditation.

CONTEMPLATION. A process that involves thinking about the meaning of thoughts, words, or objects. It is not used in TM, although it is used in other forms of meditation.

CREATIVE INTELLIGENCE. The inherent ability that guides action toward bringing about the preordained fulfillment of any living thing; for example, a cherry pit can produce nothing but a cherry tree.

COMMON STATES OF CONSCIOUSNESS. Waking, sleeping, and dreaming, as well as all altered states of waking, sleeping, and dreaming, which can be defined mainly by the physiological changes they produce in the body. These differ considerably from the physiological changes produced by TM.

COSMIC CONSCIOUSNESS. The goal of all meditators. It is the development of the field of pure consciousness, through meditation, to the point where one is living in a state of Being at all times.

DEEP SLEEP. A state in which all physical body functions slow down and the mind lacks any experience.

EVOLUTION. In meditation, a process wherein life increases in energy, intelligence, and total fulfillment.

GURU. A term normally used by the pupil to refer to his instructor. It is not used generally in TM because this technique does not involve a close relationship between master and disciple. Usually used to refer to the teacher of Maharishi Mahesh Yogi, the Guru Dev.

INITIATE. To impart the technique to an individual so he may begin meditating.

IMS. The International Meditation Society, an organization set up by the Maharishi to teach TM.

MAHARISHI. A Hindu term meaning great sage, saint, or seer.

MAHARISHI MAHESH YOGI. The prime exponent of transcendental meditation. He is responsible for making the technique available throughout the world and is the founder of the science of creative intelligence.

MAHARISHI INTERNATIONAL UNIVERSITY. The structure that
has been set up to provide an educational framework
for the teaching of creative intelligence. Credits are
transferable to a limited number of American colleges
and universities.

MANTRA. A suitable sound, imparted during personal instruction by a teacher, which, through proper use,
enables an individual to experience increasingly
subtler states of consciousness and thereby transcend
to the source of thought.

MEDITATION. Any mental process that leads an individual
to a state of greater awareness and potential.

METABOLIC RATE. A number of measurable physical processes that help determine the state the body is in.
During TM the metabolic rate of the body, as measured by oxygen consumption, drops approximately 20
percent.

OM. A mantra used in most forms of meditation, but not
in TM because, according to the Maharishi, it leads
to inaction rather than action.

PHYSIOLOGY. A branch of biology dealing with the organic
processes and phenomena that take place within the
organism or any of its parts.

PUJA. A ceremony of gratitude that is performed at the
time of initiation, honoring a tradition of masters who
have maintained the purity of transcendental meditation.

RESIDENCE COURSES. Instruction, usually held over a prolonged period of time, which provides an opportunity
for greater understanding and experience of meditation. They are usually held on weekends. Also known
as "advances."

SAMADHI. The Sanskrit term for Being, the goal of all
forms of meditation. It is also known as nirvana and
satori.

SCIENCE OF CREATIVE INTELLIGENCE. A systematic study
of the nature, development, and application of crea-

tive intelligence, as it manifests itself in various fields of learning and modes of life.

SELF-HYPNOSIS. A process that involves autosuggestion or control to produce some desired change in the mental attitude. It has no relationship to TM.

SIMS. The Students' International Meditation Society, the fastest growing student movement in the United States, whose sole purpose is to make TM available at high schools and colleges.

SOURCE OF THOUGHT. The basis of thinking and the center of creative intelligence; it is reached by transcending the subtlest thought impulse. See *Being*.

SRM. The Spiritual Regeneration Movement, another branch of TM teaching, founded by the Maharishi in England.

STRESS. A physical, chemical, or emotional factor, that which may cause physical and mental tension. It is relieved through regular meditation.

SUBTLER LEVELS OF CONSCIOUSNESS. Refined degrees of existence; levels at which a thought may be understood in a more exact form.

THOUGHT. An intimate object of experience, which is continually changing in an individual's consciousness, and can exhibit creative intelligence and energy.

TRANSCEND. To go beyond; using the process of transcendental meditation, an individual experiences increasingly subtler states of thought until he "transcends" the state of thinking and arrives at a field of pure awareness.

TRANSCENDENTAL MEDITATION. A mental process that prepares an individual for activity as well as relieving accumulated stress and providing a period of deep rest.

TRANSCENDENTAL STATE OF CONSCIOUSNESS. A fourth state of consciousness, which is differentiated by the body being in a state of physical rest but the mind being awake. Also known as "restful alertness." Differs substantially from the common states of consciousness in many physical ways.

YOGA. A Hindu system of physical and mental exercises that enable an individual to obtain physical and mental control and a state of well-being.

ZEN. A form of Buddhism that enables an individual to obtain enlightenment. Also teaches self-discipline and a form of meditation that differs from TM.

ABOUT THE AUTHORS

JHAN ROBBINS is a former President of the Society of Magazine Writers and his articles, particularly in the fields of science and health, have appeared in READER'S DIGEST, MC CALLS, GOOD HOUSEKEEPING, among many others. He was co-author of the book, *An Analysis of Human Sexual Inadequacy*. Another of his books, *Eight Weeks to Live*, about the last days of the late Senator Robert A. Taft, was nominated for a Pulitzer Prize. He has also been a consultant to the Association for the Advancement of Psychoanalysis, the American Cancer Society and the White House Conference on Children.

DAVID FISHER has been a reporter for LIFE magazine and a staff writer for Joan Rivers's TV talk show. He is co-author of a novel, *The Touch Team*, and collaborated on baseball pitcher Ferguson Jenkins's book, *Inside Pitching*.